Heart of my Heart

by

Bill Harris

as told to

Joan R. Neubauer

Coming Soon from Bill Harris

A.M.A. 1944-1948

and

W. Carter Grinstead:
A Biography

Soon to follow:

Round Top, Texas

50 of My Best Hunts

The Girls I Loved But Did Not Marry

Bill Harris (signature)

Heart of my Heart

by

Bill Harris

as told to

Joan R. Neubauer

ISBN 0-9700615-7-9

Copyright 2001

Word Wright International
P.O. Box 1785
Georgetown, Texas 78627

Printed in the United States of America

Dedicated to my precious wife, Frances, who saved me.

Chapter 1

"Harris, get in there at left guard!" Coach Buddy Jungmichael shouted and threw his clipboard down. "That's the third time they've tried to run that play. When are they going to get it right?"

Ox Emerson, the other coach for the University of Texas freshman team folded his arms across his chest and shook his head in dismay. "One of these days we'll get a team with a whole brain among them."

"Harris! Left guard! Left guard! Let's try it again, ladies." Jungmichael left his companion and headed for the young warriors on the field.

Bill Harris stood up with his hands on his hips and watched the coach close the distance between them. The coach gave them a few words of instruction. Bill nodded and began to take his place. Before he'd even settled into his stance, Randall Clay, one of Texas's fast, shifty, varsity fullbacks, headed in his direction with the ball.

Bill lunged, throwing his shoulder into Clay as hard as he'd ever hit anyone at Augusta Military Academy, but what had cut it over in Virginia didn't work in Texas. Clay ran right over him without missing a beat and kept running for a ten-yard gain.

Feeling like the whole defensive line had stampeded across his body, Bill picked himself up and resumed his four-point stance for the next play.

Before the center snapped the ball, one of the varsity guys playing across from him yelled. "Hey, Coach! Get this kid out of here. All that blood's making me puke."

Bill looked down to check out his body. His jersey was blood-stained but he had no way of knowing whether the red had come from himself or someone else. Then he reached up to his face and felt the stickiness ooze from his nose. It rivered down his chin and neck and the stains on his jersey grew. He hadn't even known his nose was bleeding.

Coach Cherry took one look at him and yelled, "Jesus Christ! Get the trainer over here!"

He felt no pain but the alarm in the coach's voice sent a tremor of fear through him. "What's wrong, Coach?"

The coach led him to the sideline and turned him over to someone who held a rolled up towel against his nose. The bleeding didn't stop so they sent him down to the team doctor. By the time they got back to the locker room, the bleeding had slowed to nearly a stop but his nose had swelled to nearly twice its normal size and looked to be pointing in an odd direction.

The doctor scrutinized the injury and squinted as he poked at it.

"Ow!" The sudden pain shot through his head and Bill reached for the table behind him to steady himself.

"Sorry about that." He continued to study the broken nose. "Able to breathe a'tall?"

"No, sir. Not really."

With that, the doctor reached over to a nearby table and picked up an object that resembled a butter knife more than anything else. Bill gripped the edge of the table he sat on. He didn't know what the doctor was going to do but he had an idea it wasn't going to be pleasant.

Before Bill could ask, the doctor began shoving the blunt end of the instrument into one side of his nose. Bill kept expecting to feel the stab of pain, at any moment, but it never came. After several repetitions of this action in both nostrils, the misshapen bit of flesh and bone seemed to lift upward just a little in the air and shift back to the middle.

"That hurt, kid?" the doctor asked looking at him intently.

"No, sir. Didn't feel a thing."

The older man shook his head. "No sense, no feeling," he muttered under his breath. "Now look here, Harris, you know you're going to break that nose of yours another dozen times or so over the next four years. Don't you?"

Bill stared at him, speechless.

"Well, believe me, it's going to happen, and that's a simple fact. No sense fixing anything just yet. Come see me after you finish for good and I'll do the job right, okay?"

Bill nodded. "So you think now I'll get some protective gear for my nose?"

"Could be. I'll talk to the coach. Maybe he'll give you a nose guard to attach to your helmet now." The doctor reassembled his little black back and muttered. "Damn shame, these guys got to get hurt before they give them any gear."

"Well, you know, Doc, you can't see as well or move as fast if you're loaded down with pads and stuff," Bill said by

3

way of explanation.

"Yeah. I know all about it, so do the guys who've been hurt. Talk to the guy who broke his neck last scrimmage."

Bill nodded. He had seen many of his friends suffer severe injuries, including a fellow freshman who received a brain injury and left two of his upper teeth behind in his blocker's shoulder. He had been lucky up until now and even a broken nose was nothing to write home about.

"Just hope your luck holds out, Bill." The doctor placed his fedora back on his head and turned to leave.

"Thanks, Doc."

Heading for the door, the doctor kept moving forward but waved to the young man remaining behind. Bill hopped down from the table and headed for the nearest mirror. The sight of his broken nose shocked him. While not overly vain, he considered himself an okay looking guy, but the suddenly misshapen nose lent a whole new look to his appearance and he wondered how he'd ever get to meet any girls now.

Just then, the rest of the team began filing into the locker room.

"Harris!"

Coach Emerson's voice got his immediate attention and Bill walked over to him. "Yeah, Coach?"

Emerson took Bill's chin in his hand and gave a critical look at his nose. "You gonna live?"

"Doc says so."

"Yeah. We'll get you a nose guard for your helmet." Then without another word or gesture he turned and retreated into his office.

That evening at the training table in Hill Hall, the varsity

4

players forced Bill and his fellow freshmen to stand during the meal. He had had a tough practice and he longed to sit at his place and eat the steak and potatoes that beckoned. He managed a couple of mouthfuls before one of the upperclassmen demanded a rousing rendition of the "UT Fight Song" from the freshmen.

The freshmen all looked at each other and broke into song. After the last chorus, Bill made another attempt at his meal. Once the upperclassmen had lost interest in the freshmen, they left the dining room and these poor, hungry creatures to down a cold dinner and warm milk.

"Are they ever going to get tired of this crap?" one of Bill's dining companions asked.

"Not anytime soon." Bill shook his head and ate his meal as fast as he could before some upperclassman decided he wanted to hear a version of "Melancholy Baby."

His feelings about football were quickly changing. He had loved playing at Augusta, but here, it seemed that everyone from the coaches to the upperclassmen did their best to make him hate it. Why couldn't anything in his life go the way it was "supposed to go?" Not even his parents had been a stabilizing force in his life.

He had loved living in New York, probably the world's most exciting city. He had thought their family had a good life. His father was a doctor with a thriving practice and they lived in an apartment overlooking Central Park, but that was all cut short by problems between his parents and they had moved to Houston hoping against hope that no one there would know their little secret. He had heard his parents argue time and time again.

Sometimes they argued in his presence, sometimes late at night when they thought he was asleep, but he heard through the walls and down the hall.

"No, I won't give you a divorce!" his mother's shrill voice came at him. "Why should I? So you can marry her?"

"She has a name," his father yelled back. "Her name is Dale!"

"And to think, I never had any idea that you were carrying on with your nurse. How could you have done that to me?"

"To you? What do you think you've been doing to me all these years?"

"And then you promised to marry her, so then she sued you for breach of promise, and she won! You had to sell off two thousand acres of your father's farm near Fulshear to pay off the judgment she won. And no matter what anybody says, we both know that your little episode caused you to be passed over for the chairmanship of the dermatology department."

They'd argued long into the night and Bill wondered what held them together anymore. He would wrap his pillow around his head and roll over to fall asleep.

The scandal had first surfaced about the time Bill was graduating from Public School #6, probably the most famous elementary school in New York City, and it had changed his whole life.

From his youngest days, he had always been told he'd go on to Brooklyn Technical School to prepare himself to study pre-med in college, and then go on to medical school. But the scandal had caused his mother to fall into a deep depression which necessitated her hospitalization. His father spent his

6

time with his lover and on the golf course and packed Bill off to Augusta Military School where his grandfather had graduated from in the early 1900's. Now he had no idea what his future held.

After they eventually moved to Houston, his mother began to worry about how their Houston relatives might gossip around their bridge tables at the country club, particularly his aunts, wives of his four doctor uncles.

He wondered if his history would follow them wherever they went and if they'd be exiled and ostracized and sneered at for something he had nothing to do with. Then he found he had a talent for football and was offered twenty football scholarships.

It wasn't easy, but he settled on the University of Texas and looked forward to majoring in pre-med. He viewed this as a second chance. No one would know him there. No one would know about the problems his parents had. He would prosper or fail on his own as a pre-med major, and he looked forward to a fresh start.

Chapter 2

The campus seemed especially beautiful that afternoon. One by one, orange and gold leaves drifted to the ground as the trees readied themselves for the coming winter sleep. Bill Harris flecked a leaf from his shoulder as he made his way across the broad expanse of the University of Texas at Austin to the Pi Phi house.

Located close to the campus, the Pi Phi house, an expansive, three-story colonial structure, its white brick and columns impressed all who saw it. Bill stood for a few short seconds looking up at the house then took the steps two at a time before entering the foyer. Immediately he spotted the woman sitting behind the reception desk and headed for her.

She lifted her gaze from the book she was reading to address him. "May I help you?"

Bill let a tinge of nervousness show as he ran his fingers through his red hair. "Ma'am, would you please see if Patsy Capps is in today, and if she is, could she come down and see me a minute?" There he said it. Now he could take a breath.

"Your name?" Her tone could have frozen ice cream in the middle of July.

Bill swallowed. "Please tell her Bill Harris is here to see her." He looked down at his shoes that sunk into the plush blue carpet.

The woman picked up the phone and dialed a number he couldn't see. "Patsy Capps, please."

Bill heard someone yell on the phone. "Patsy Capps!"

A moment went by and the woman began speaking. "Patsy, there's a Bill Harris here to see you. Do you have time to visit with him? Uh, huh. Uh, huh. Sure. I'll hold." She contrived a smile that made Bill shuffle his feet uncomfortably.

Upstairs, Frances sat on the bed of a girlfriend talking when she heard all the commotion. "What's going on out here?" she said as she headed for the hall. She saw Patsy on the phone.

"I've got a red-headed football player here. Anybody want him?" Patsy called to her sorority sisters.

Girls giggled up and down the hall.

"What's he look like?" one girl asked.

"He can't be that bad, Patsy," another commented, shouting down the hall.

Finally, Frances volunteered. "I'll take him."

Patsy said, "You sure?"

Frances nodded. Patsy turned and spoke into the phone. Frances said her good-byes to her friend and headed down the stairs.

At the front desk, Bill waited nervously for an answer. The woman behind the desk smiled and his spirits soared. "Just a minute," she said. "You can wait over there."

"Thank you, ma'am." Bill took a deep breath in relief. He had met Patsy in Galveston several summers ago and hoped she remembered him.

9

They had met when he visited his uncle, Dr. Titus Harris. The Harris family and the Capps family were good friends and they had introduced the young people. While Patsy and Bill had not grown close on those occasions, they had been friendly and enjoyed each other's company. He thought this might be the perfect opportunity to renew that acquaintance and perhaps help it blossom into a deeper friendship.

He smoothed out the sleeves of his white cotton shirt and straightened his collar. He wanted to make a good impression, after all, but then thought of his nose and what Patsy would say when she saw him. No sooner had he settled himself into an overstuffed, uncomfortable chair, when he noticed a beautiful young woman heading toward him. He stood as she approached.

Tall, with dark hair and huge brown eyes that seemed shinier than any human eyes had the right to be. Though she dressed like any other college girl, bobby socks, penny loafers, a skirt well below the knees, and a bright pullover sweater with a scarf around her neck, he recognized that her demure outfit hid a gorgeous figure.

"Hi," she said extending her hand.

He swallowed hard. The moment Bill took it, he thought it was the softest thing he'd ever felt in his life. "Hi, I'm Bill, but you're not Patsy."

Her giggle sounded like music. "No, I'm afraid Patsy has to study for a big test tomorrow, so she asked me to tell you how sorry she is that she can't see you. My name is Frances. I hope you're not too disappointed."

He noticed her voice, a cross between singing and laughing all at the same time, and he thought his heart would melt.

"We'll glad to. . .make. . .I mean, happy to. . . I'm Bill," he finally said. He couldn't put more than three words together and when he did, he stuttered all over the place.

She laughed. "Why don't we go for a walk, Bill? Let's go over to The Drag." She reached for his hand to encourage him.

It took only a few minutes to walk over to The Drag, a section of Guadalupe Street between 19th and 24th that ran in front of the Varsity Theater.

"You have the most wonderful accent, Bill," she sang again as they strolled. "Where in the world are you from?"

He stumbled and almost fell. He knew he'd have to look where he was going instead of staring at her. "I was born in New York City, but went to high school in Virginia, a military school. Then my parents moved back to Houston, where my father lived until he graduated from med school and went up north to practice."

"My oldest brother, Nelson went to prep school in Virginia too. Staunton Military Academy. Could that be the one you went to?"

Bill shook his head. "No, I went to Augusta Military. One of my grandfathers graduated from there way back, early 1900s. I guess Dad thought that it was good enough for my grandfather, it should be a pretty good place for me too."

"But, before that you lived in New York City. How exciting!" She made it sound as though New York City were the most exotic place in the world. "But where did you live? I mean, my parents went up to New York for a week one time and all they talked about when they got back was the

11

shopping and Broadway, and Central Park, and Rockefeller Center, and all the museums. It just sounded so exciting, but not like a place where anybody could really have a house to live in," she trilled.

A quick peek at her face told him her enthusiasm was real. "Well, see, we lived in these big apartments, different ones over the years, right there on Fifth Avenue, overlooking Central Park." He told her in his most important voice as though proud he could lay claim to something so glamorous to her.

Together, Bill and Frances moved through the crowds that gathered along the drag. Traffic moved up and down the avenue. Horns blared. Engines roared. Street vendors touted their wares, but Bill was only aware of this beautiful girl who walked beside him.

"So where did you go to school?" Bill asked.

"I went to high school at Gulf Park School for Women in Mississippi. Then I spent my first year of college there. I came to UT as a sophomore and pledged my mother's sorority."

"Your mother was a Pi Phi?"

Frances nodded.

Bill pointed to himself. "So was my mother, but I'm not exactly sure what year," Bill said shyly.

"My goodness, I wonder if they knew each other."

The delight in her voice warmed Bill's heart and he squeezed her hand. As they approached Naus Drug Store, Bill steered her toward the counter. "Can I treat you to a drink?"

Frances smiled her most intoxicating smile and nodded. "Why thank you, Bill. I'd love one."

The druggist walked behind the fountain and greeted the two young people. "Good afternoon. What can I get for you two kids?" he asked as he wiped the counter down.

Bill turned to Frances. "What would you like?"

"A cherry coke, please."

Bill beamed. "A cherry coke for the lady and a regular coke for me."

"You got it."

The druggist turned to make the ordered drinks and Bill turned to Frances who was smiling at him. Bill thought his heart stood still and stared. The sound of something being pushed toward him broke the spell.

"That'll be ten cents," the man behind the counter said.

Bill reached in his pocket and brought out two nickels and slid them across the counter and turned back to Frances. He was not aware of anything around him but her and he started staring again.

"Bill? Bill?" Frances tried to bring him out of his trance.

He abruptly cleared his throat. "Sorry. I was just thinking about something."

"What, Bill? Tell me what you were thinking."

"Nothing much," he finally answered. How could he tell her that he thought she was the most beautiful girl he had ever seen? How could he tell her he could picture himself spending the rest of his life with her? Could he? Of course he couldn't.

Frances sipped on her straw. "So why did your parents send you to school in Virginia?"

"Well, to tell you the truth, my mother got kind of sick. Doctors said she was 'depressed' and they put her in a kind of hospital for about a year. So Dad decided I'd be better off in a boarding school instead of alone with him in our apartment. So, that's just kind of what happened."

His voice trailed off and he looked through the storefront window to the street hoping to avoid any disapproval from Frances. He also knew he had just told a lie but couldn't bring himself to talk about his father or his string of "lady friends." He didn't want to think about how his father's latest and longest love affair had affected his mother. It made him sick to think of his father with another woman and every time he thought about it he felt his disgust and anger grow.

He thought he'd take a lesson from Scarlett O'Hara and think about it tomorrow. Right now he was with Frances and he turned his attention back to her.

"Tell me about yourself. Where did you come from? Tell me about yourself, your family. I want to know all about you."

The creamy complexion of Frances's cheeks turned slightly pink and Bill thought her reaction to talking about herself most endearing.

"Oh, I'm just a country girl, Bill. I grew up on a farm between Luling and San Marcos, right down on the river. After that, when I finished elementary school, we moved up to Midland, my father got a job as a federal prosecutor up there.

"Daddy had a law degree from Texas. And he, well, he had some sort of financial reverses. That happens in the oil business, you know."

"God knows, I understand," Bill said. He nodded to encourage her to continue.

"Daddy was a football player at Texas a long time ago too, like you are, and my older brother."

The mention of football got Bill's attention. "Really? I mean, what did they play? What position?"

"Daddy was a quarterback, way, way back, like 1910 or something like that."

As Bill smiled and nodded he wondered what she'd think if he told her how miserable he was playing football. He forced it from his mind. "And your brother, what position?"

Frances giggled. "I'm ashamed to admit it but I'm really not sure what it was called. He's so much older than I am. Twelve years is a lot when you're kids. But I know he was some kind of runner."

She stared at him with a question in her eyes. "Maybe halfback. Is there such a position?" She blushed.

"Sure is," he said. In the back of his mind he uttered a little prayer. Thank God she didn't worship jocks.

Bill and Frances talked about their families, vacations, friends, college, school, and all manner of things long after their cokes had disappeared when Frances looked outside.

"Oh my goodness, it must be getting late." She looked at her watch to confirm her suspicion. "It is, Bill. We've been here for more than an hour and I've got to get back."

"It's early yet," he protested. "Not even dinner time yet."

"Really, this has been great, Bill, but I have to get back. I have things to do."

Disappointed that his time had been cut short, Bill relented. "All right. Let me walk you back."

In a hurry, Frances picked up the pace of their walk until they arrived at Mrs. Bells' Boarding House.

"Well, at least I know where you live now," Bill chuckled.

"Yes, you do."

He wanted to reach out and touch her face. He wanted to run his fingers through her hair. Good Lord, he wanted to hold her in his arms and kiss her until she fainted. But the nagging thought that Mrs. Bell might be watching from the window cowered him. Instead, he reached to shake her hand and felt his insides tremble with the contact. "Could I have your phone number?"

Frances smiled in her intoxicating way and reached into her pocket for a slip of paper. "Got a pencil?"

Frantically, Bill searched his pockets and came up with a sorry nub of what had once been a pencil and handed it to her. With a gentle touch, Frances took it from his fingers and wrote her number down then handed him the slip of paper and pencil back.

"Thanks again, Bill. Maybe I'll see you around again," and she turned and ran up the step to the house.

"Yeah. Maybe you will," but he knew his words had fallen on deaf ears. She had already closed the door behind her. "Darn right you'll see me again," and he turned toward his dorm, Hill Hall.

Bill never knew the campus could look so beautiful or the air smell so sweet. He had never walked with so light a step or so happy a heart. Once more he looked back over his shoulder to Mrs. Bell's Boarding House. Although he was already out of sight he smiled to himself knowing that Frances was in that general direction.

Frances rushed up the stairs of the boarding house to her second floor room. A quick glance at her watch told her she only had twenty minutes to get ready for her date. She flew down the hall and bumped into Mary, the girl who lived next door to her.

"Frances! Where've you been?" Mary asked trying to steady herself.

"Out with a friend."

"Bob's been calling?"

"Who?" Then Frances remembered. "Oh, yeah, my date. What did he want?"

""Said he was just checking to make sure you two were still on for this evening."

Frances checked her watch again. "I'll be ready." She ran into her room and headed for her closet and Mary followed.

"I thought you were at the Pi Phi House," Mary said as she sat on Frances's bed.

"I was."

"You must have had a great time over there to forget about your date." Mary nonchalantly filed her nails with an emery board.

"I wasn't there for long." Looking in the mirror she adjusted the scarf around her neck and ran a brush through her hair.

"So where'd you go?"

Annoyed, Frances turned to her friend. "Why all the questions?"

"Because you look different?"

"Different?" Frances looked at herself closely in the mirror.

"Yeah. Brighter. Happier somehow."

She couldn't control the warmth that flowed through her and knew she was blushing. Her mother was right. She wore her emotions on her face as clearly as a printed page.

Mary stood up and clapped her hands. "I knew it! You met somebody and it wasn't Bob. Who was it? Tell me all about him."

"I don't have time right now. I've got to get ready for my date." Frances touched up her face powder and lipstick.

"Come on, Frances. You can give me a name." Mary now stood right behind her and was looking at her in the mirror.

"Okay. He's a football player."

"Oooh. Do tell. What's his name?"

"Bill." She placed a dab of perfume behind her ear.

"Is he cute?"

"Very." She smoothed her skirt.

"What's his major?"

"Pre-med."

"Even better, a doctor," Mary crooned. "So tell me more about him," she said anxiously.

Frances paused a moment and looked off into space as though trying to picture him in her mind. "He's tall. No, he's huge! He's a football player. He has red hair and very handsome. He's got a smile that, well, it makes you happy just to look at him. And his manners are wonderful."

The phone in the hall rang and Frances and Mary looked at each other. "He's here," they said in unison.

"I'll get it. You don't want to seem to anxious," Mary

said as she headed for the phone.

Frances grabbed for her purse and added a handkerchief while she listened to the conversation in the hall.

"Okay, Bob. I'll tell her you're here. She'll be down in a couple of minutes."

When Frances looked up, Mary stood at the doorway. "Your date's here."

"I heard."

"Did you tell Bill you had another date?"

Frances gave her friend a horrified look. "Good Lord, no!"

"Just asking."

"See you later." Frances walked down the hall toward the stairs. Yes, she would have a good time at the movies with Bob tonight. Why not? He was tall, good looking, and had great prospects. He would make a great husband. But.. .and then her thoughts flew to the boy she had just met this afternoon, he wasn't Bill.

*   *   *

Bill walked into the front door of Hill Hall and realized everyone was heading for the dining room.

"Hey, Harris! Hurry up. You're gonna be late for dinner."

Without acknowledging who had reminded him about the upcoming meal, Bill ran up the stairs to wash his hands. Washing his hands before sitting down to a meal had been drilled into him as a child and he couldn't bring himself to do otherwise.

In the dining room, nearly everyone was already seated

and Bill headed for his usual spot. He reached for his napkin as he sat and spread it across his lap. The action brought to mind the many lessons about manners his mother had taught him and he smiled.

"So where you been, Harris?" his roommate asked as he speared a second pork chop from the platter that had been passed around the table.

"Out," Bill answered simply.

"A girl?" someone else at the table asked.

"Geesh! Look at that nose. Who'd go out with him?" They all laughed at his expense.

Only the most beautiful girl in the world, Bill thought, and he grinned good naturedly as he placed peas on his plate and passed them to his left.

"Marino said he saw you walking on The Drag with a girl. A real looker," his roommate said.

"Yep." Bill reached for his water glass.

"Is that all you can say?" another one of his dining companions asked.

"Yep."

His roommate poked the ribs of the student sitting next to him. "This one must be special. No kiss and tell."

"I never kiss and tell."

Bill finished the rest of his meal amid the good-natured ribbing of his friends.

"Come on, Harris. Finish up. We've got a practice to go to."

Bill only half-listened to the conversation going on around him. Talk of plays for the upcoming game, classes, professors, and girls swirled around him. He ignored them while he ate his dinner. How could he talk to anybody right now. He had met the most beautiful girl in the world and she seemed to like him.

"Done yet, Harris?"

Bill looked up to see the quarterback standing over him. He nodded. Taking a last swig of his milk, Bill followed his teammates upstairs to grab their football gear.

Chapter 3

For the entire week after his first encounter with Frances, Bill could think of little else. The sound of her voice, the sparkle in her eyes, the scent of her hair, haunted him from morning until night. He wanted to ask her out for a date, but wondered how he could accomplish that without money or a car. He knew that if he didn't do something fast, some good looking guy with a car would snatch her up and she'd be out of his life forever.

Finally, when he could stand it no longer, he picked up the phone and called Mrs. Bell's, the rooming house where Frances lived. Even if he couldn't take her on a date just yet, he had to keep seeing her one way or the other. With each ring of the phone he clenched his fist in anticipation, hoping she would say yes to seeing him again. Finally, someone answered.

"Hello, could I speak with Frances, please?" he asked politely.

"Sure. Hold on."

Bill drummed his fingers against his knee nervously. She couldn't turn him down. Could she?

"Hello."

Her music came over the wires and it thrilled him as no

other voice had before. He cleared his throat and his head. "Hello, Frances. This is Bill Harris." Lord he hoped she remembered who he was.

"Oh, hello, Bill. How are you?"

She did remember! "Fine on such a beautiful day. I thought it might be nice to go for a walk tonight, like after supper." Involuntarily he crossed his fingers.

"Why, Bill. What a nice idea."

His spirits soared and he thought he felt his heart skip a beat, then as calmly as he could said, "I'll pick you up around seven. Okay?"

"Great. See you then."

Bill hung up the phone and sank to the floor with his back against the wall. He wiped the beads of perspiration from his forehead, thankful that she had not only remembered him, but that she had said yes.

That evening, he gulped his dinner and rushed back to his room to freshen up. With one last look in the mirror, he combed an errant lock of red from his temple, glanced at his watch, and raced out the door with Mrs. Bell's as his destination.

When he walked up the to house, he saw Frances on the front porch, talking with some friends. He found it tough enough facing her alone, but with all her friends around he didn't quite know how to act. He took a deep breath and walked up to the porch as though he owned the place, a real reach, but he figured it was the only way to approach the situation.

"Hello, Frances," he said as he walked up the steps.

Her smile deepened her dimples. "Well, hello, Bill." She

took a quick look at her watch. "And right on time." She said her good-byes to her friends and walked toward Bill.

"I was hoping I wasn't too early," he said sheepishly.

"No, I decided you were right. It is a lovely night so thought I'd get a head start on the evening."

"Then let's get started," he said with a broad smile.

Side by side they strolled, never looking at each other, never touching, until they reached the UT clock tower in the middle of the campus. The tall, imposing figure that stood in the middle of the campus loomed overhead. Tonight, white lights would bathe its uppermost spires since UT didn't have a game. But when they played, and when they won, bright orange lights splashed across the night sky to announce the football team's victory.

"Here's a nice spot." Bill pointed to a mossy old tree. Tall though it was, it sat overshadowed by the great tower. There, without exchanging a single word, they sat, resting their backs against that stately tree. Legs stretched companionably in front of them, they listened to the bell chiming the quarter, then the half hour.

When Frances closed her eyes and sighed, she took Bill's breath away. He had to spend more time with her and he had to suggest something better than a walk each time. He did some quick calculations in his head and made a decision, though it took him a few minutes to work up the courage. "Frances, would you like to go to the movies on Saturday?"

Frances opened her eyes and clapped her hands together. "Oh, what fun!"

"Terrific. I'll find out what's playing and when and call you tomorrow."

They spent the rest of the evening talking about classes, and friends, and activities, and gradually, Bill grew more at ease in her company. While he was thoroughly enjoying this time with her, he looked forward to a real date this weekend.

Three days later, the weekend came and Bill was beside himself with anticipation. He showered and shaved, and combed his hair and combed his hair again. The 2:00 matinee couldn't get here soon enough as far as Bill was concerned. When he heard the bell tower chime 1:30, he confirmed the time with his watch and headed for Mrs. Bell's.

He whistled all the way, and noticed a lightness to his step that had not been there before. He truly liked Frances, but was he falling in love with her? How could he not have realized it before? He wanted to be with her, know all about her, spend the rest of his life with her. Of course he was in love. How could he not be? His challenge now was to not scare her away with his exuberance.

They had decided to see a John Wayne movie. Bill almost found sitting in the darkened theater with Frances so close, overwhelming. He wanted to drape his arm across her shoulder and hold her close. Instead, halfway through the movie he reached for her hand and she gave it willingly. They sat like that until the end.

"So what did you think of the movie?" Bill asked on their walk back to the boarding house.

"Oh, I liked it a lot. Really enjoyed it." Then she stared humming some military tune, one that Bill recognized but couldn't name.

She surprised him when she slipped her hand back into his and led the way in pumping their arms in time to the music as though they were soldiers on parade. They kept step with the exaggerated swing of their arms and the music all the way back to the boarding house. He felt like a fool because he couldn't stop staring at the way their hands looked together. What a wonderful sight. Together. Though to the rest of the world he realized they must have painted quite a picture, but he didn't care. His money was gone until the first of December, but he didn't care about that either. He was with Frances, the love of his life.

A simple walk. A single movie. But he couldn't get her out of his mind. He had to see her again, somehow, someway, even if only under some pretext.

The next day, Bill just happened to be walking by the boarding house when he decided to stop in to see her, or so he said. Of course, that had been his intention from the start.

"Bill, what a nice surprise. I was just thinking of you," Frances said as she came down the stairs.

She couldn't have said anything nicer to him. If he could have, he probably would have curled his toes with delight. "I've been thinking about you too," he said. "I was just walking by and stopped in to see you, that is, if you're not too busy."

"Oh, no. I've been studying. It's time to take a break. Ever play ping pong, Bill?"

He chuckled. "A little, and not very well."

"We have some ping pong tables in the sunroom at the sorority house. They let us have boys come by to visit and I thought it might be fun to find out which one of us plays worse," she smiled up at him mischievously.

If she hadn't been there, right in front of him, he would

26

have jumped for joy. She wanted to see him again. She must like him, at least a little. He couldn't believe it.

Neither of them played very well that night, but by the end of the evening, they were clinging to one another, laughing, moaning, trying to catch their breath.

"You let me win, Bill Harris," she accused.

Bill held up his hands in a gesture of denial. "I didn't. I swear it. I told you I was no good. Now you know for sure."

She planted her hands firmly on her hips and glared at him. "I think you found yourself a bookie and bet on me to win so that you had to throw the game. Isn't that right?"

He shook his head. "Oh, yeah, right. Bet my ten dollar a month allowance at a hundred to one odds that you'd win, threw the game and now I'm set for life. Why don't we go look at new cars?"

Frances began to laugh again. When she had regained control, she said, "In the interest of fair play, we have to have a rematch. Let's call it the 'DKE-Pi Phi International ping pong championship."

"You're on. Name your date and time."

Frances stood on tiptoe and looked up at him, but the tip of her head only came to his neck. "Right after dinner tomorrow night."

"You got it!"

Bill had very little experience around girls. Augusta Military Academy had been an all male four-year prep school, and none of the girls he had ever known from other schools had a sense of humor like hers. And she was so pretty. He often wondered what he had done right to deserve her attention. He couldn't stop thinking about her.

27

Even though Bill's roommate, Dick Austin, had a girl in Denton, he tagged along with Bill and Frances the next night. In return, Frances found another member of her pledge class who could play ping pong so their tournament turned out to be a doubles match.

"Point!" Bill yelled. "We won. We are the new champions."

"So you are, but now I demand my share of the winnings."

He gave her a puzzled look.

"You know you made a huge bet with your bookie again. I want my share." She walked toward him with her palm held up.

Bill reached into his pocket and found a dime. When he placed it in her hand he said, "It's my last."

Frances took it with a giggle. Bill knew she had no idea he was telling the truth. He must be in love. He had given her his last dime. But it did come back to him. She used it to treat Bill to a Coke at the drugstore afterwards.

A few days later, they went for another walk and plowed through another game of ping pong. Neither one of them had improved any, but they had a great time together. When Bill finally received his December allowance, he took her to see another movie. That night they walked more slowly than ever back to Mrs. Bell's.

The boys who dated girls at the boarding house had learned the trick of arriving at the front door of the boarding house a minute or two before the magic hour of midnight and standing around until the University clock began to chime the hour. As soon as they heard them, they kissed their date goodnight, and when the last note faded, shoved her inside to the house mother who was always waiting right there to snap the latch closed as soon as the last girl made it in.

That night, Bill pulled Frances close to him and the door and kissed her on the mouth, quick as a wink, before he pushed her inside. He staggered all the way back to Hill Hall, drunk with joy. He couldn't believe his good luck.

Other than a girl named, Gay, a boarding student at nearby Stuart Hall in Staunton, Virginia, Bill had never had a date in his life, and those had consisted of a few joy rides with Carter Wood, his best friend and roommate at AMA, and his girlfriend in a car they had more or less "borrowed" from one of the coaches. Bill figured it was an all right thing to do, especially since the coach had shown him where he hid the key. He had also taken Gay to a few dances, but that was as far as their relationship had ever gone.

This lack of experience led Bill to look upon Frances as his first real girlfriend, the first girl he'd taken on a real date, and the first girl he'd ever really kissed. He had to see her everyday, or his life was not complete.

Chapter 4

The university closed for Christmas in mid December, and Bill paled at the thought of not seeing Frances for weeks until the new semester began. Frances would be going home to Midland, and he to his family in Houston. But they promised to write while they were apart and look forward to seeing each other again in January.

Bill found his parting from Frances physically painful. The hollow in his chest left him bereft and he had no idea how he'd get through the Christmas holidays without her, but his mother had an idea.

"Bill, I'm so glad you're home. I've missed you, and I know it's not as exciting here as it is at school, but I have just the thing to keep you busy," his mother babbled on.

Bill only looked at her in silence wondering what she had in mind.

"Look, this should keep you busy while you're home." She handed him a stack of immaculate white envelopes addressed to him.

Bill took them from her and rifled through them. In the space of a heartbeat he looked up at his mother who beamed at him in anticipation of his pleasure, but he disappointed her. "Mother, these are invitations. . . ."

"Engraved invitations," she broke in.

"Yeah, to debutante balls all over town. There must be twelve of them here." He fanned the stack like a deck of cards.

"Isn't it wonderful. You're so popular. Most of them are to be held at River Oaks Country Club, and look, each enclosure card already has the name of your date."

"But, Mother," he protested. . . .

"Now, Bill. This is a wonderful opportunity for you," his mother insisted.

"But we only moved here a year-and-a-half ago. I didn't go to school with these people. They don't know me from any other guy on the street. I'd be among total strangers."

"Bill, you're an outgoing, fun-loving young man. I have every confidence that you'll do just fine. In fact, before the end of the first ball, everyone will know you and you'll count them among your friends."

Bill knew better than to argue with his mother any further. She had made up her mind and no one or nothing could dissuade her. With a great sigh, he walked up to his room, resigned to the fact that this would be the most miserable Christmas holiday of his life.

The first girl he had been invited to escort was Lucy Williamson. In that inimical manner of mothers, she informed him that Lucy lived in a huge mansion on Remington Avenue, close to Rice University. At her suggestion, he paid a brief visit to Lucy and her parents a few days before the ball. At least he'd know what she looked like. She was a pretty girl with a friendly personality, and in other circumstances, he might have even grown to like her, but he missed Frances

31

much too much.

On the night of the ball, Bill's father chauffeured the young couple to the country club because Bill could not yet drive. Bill found the whole experience excruciating, and constantly tugged at the collar of his tuxedo shirt, held a bit too tight by the formal tie. All the way to the country club, Bill cast nervous sidelong glances in the direction of his date and gave her an occasional, polite smile when they made eye contact. Then he caught sight of the River Oaks Country Club as his father pulled into the sweeping, circular driveway.

Lights at the top of elegant posts lit the way, and the headlights of so many cars added to the festive atmosphere, but it seemed to Bill that the collar of his shirt only grew tighter as they drew nearer. As their car pulled up to the front of the building that reminded Bill of a grand, old Southern mansion, complete with huge while pillars on the portico, Bill could not help but notice the frenzy of activity. From his back seat perch, Bill leaned forward to get a better view. He had passed this grand old building many times, but never had he seen it in quite this light.

A dozen young black men, each in an immaculate white coat, stood at the ready to open car doors, assist the ladies, take coats at the door, and hold the massive front door of the country club open for the guests. Young ladies in expensive gowns and glittering tiaras stepped from cars and gently placed their hand on their escort's arm. Young men in tuxedos gently led their date up the few steps and through the front doors.

When his father brought the car to a halt in front of the antebellum style mansion, Bill gulped hard. He didn't dare let

Formal Dances Honor Young People

For the sixth consecutive year Garrett Hamill celebrated his birthday with a formal dance at the River Oaks Country Club. Garrett, who is 18, will graduate from Kinkaid in June. His parents are Mr. and Mrs. Claud B. Hamill. In the picture on the left, from right to left, are Ronald Bartlett and Janet Jones, Garrett and Lucille Mellinger. Among the many formals honoring home from school students during the holidays was the one given at the Bayou Club in honor of Miss Pat Peterkin, Miss Betty Peckinpaugh and Miss Frances Bradley. The three girls are students at the University of Texas. In the picture to the right are from left to right Pat, Frances and Patty welcoming Lucy Wray and Bill Harris.

Newspaper clipping from the "River Oaks Times." Bill Harris and his date Lucy are seen in the picture on the right.

on how much he dreaded the coming evening so he smiled and let the young man in the white jacket open the door for him.

"Good evening, sir," the valet greeted him.

Bill smiled and nodded. "Good evening." He stood up straight and took a deep breath of the December air, then turned and reached for his date's hand. "Can I help you, Lucy?"

Lucy, ready and waiting, answered by placing her hand in Bill's. With a gentle tug, he helped her up and out of the car.

"My goodness, all these flounces sure make it hard for a girl to do much of anything." She giggled shyly. With one hand, she expertly pulled her stole more tightly around her bare shoulders. "Oh, listen."

Bill halted a moment and heard what Lucy had called to his attention. "Sounds like a great band."

"Sounds wonderful."

The valet closed the car door and Bill waved good-bye to his father, knowing he'd be back at midnight to take them home. A valet opened the door for a couple several feet ahead of them and the music grew louder, and Bill's dread grew stronger.

"Good evening, sir, mademoiselle," a valet greeted them at the door. "May I take your wrap?" he said reaching for Lucy's Persian lamb stole. At the same time he took the stole, he handed Bill a small stub.

Bill looked at the small piece of paper in his hand with a puzzled expression.

"That's to claim my wrap when we leave," Lucy whispered.

"Oh, yes, of course." Of course he knew that. It just all happened so fast. A throng of people, all strangers, surrounded him, and the music came at him ever louder, and his heart thumped harder in his chest. He wondered how he'd ever let his mother talk him into this. He took a deep breath and calmed himself.

Arm in arm, Bill and Lucy stepped down into the sunken ballroom where Bill halted a moment to take in the sight of the huge room with crystal chandeliers hung from the ceiling, formal furniture, and beautiful flower arrangements of red and white poinsettias for the Christmas season. Then he felt Lucy tug at his sleeve.

"Bill, the receiving line," she said as she led the way introducing him to everyone along the way.

"Do you know everybody in town?" Bill whispered to Lucy between handshakes.

"I don't know these people very well. They're friends of my parents though, so I'm at least expected to know their names."

The line seemed interminable and by the end of it, Bill felt as though his smile had been pasted to his face. Sounds of the orchestra playing soft music acted as background to the noise of polite chatter among polite people. The flash of cameras punctuated the soft lights of the room and Bill found himself blinking against the sudden lights at every turn.

Just as Bill turned away from the receiving line with Lucy, a flash went off in his face. He held his hand up to protect his eyes, but was too late.

"Now, Miss, give me your name and the name of your handsome young friend here, would you please?" the

35

photographer asked.

Bill was still blinking his eyes, trying to get his vision back when Lucy answered the request. Apparently, she had memorized his name from the card enclosed with her invitation. "I'm Lucy Williamson and my escort is William McGregor Harris."

Taken aback by the formality, Bill broke in "Gosh, Bill Harris would do just fine." But he wasn't quick enough.

Lucy didn't take his arm as they made their way past more people.

"Shall we find a table?" Bill suggested.

"That would be fine," Lucy said. "How about right here?"

Bill helped Lucy seat herself and then sat beside her. Bill felt as though he were stranded on a remote island of Christmas greenery, colored lights, and miles and miles of bright red ribbon and tried to make conversation with his date.

"So you've lived in Houston all your life." He knew that was a stupid way to begin, but at the moment, it was the best he could offer.

"Well, I guess you could say that," she said with a smile.

Bill gave her a puzzled look.

"Gosh, either you live someplace or you don't, wouldn't you say, Lucy?"

"Well, Bill, it's this way. You saw how big the lawns are on Remington Lane where we live?"

He nodded.

"I mean, it wasn't as if we could just run next door and play. Most of us couldn't even see the house next door. The yards are so big, you know. And my parents, well, they always wanted to know who people were and who their parents were and what they did, and, and then after elementary school, they sent me away to school in Virginia, so. . . ."

He nodded again, this time more sympathetically, but before he could say anything, she finished in a rush. "So the few friends I made in elementary school, I suppose I just sort of lost touch with them over the years."

"How long were you in Virginia?" Bill asked.

"Six years, off and on. Four years in prep school and then at Hollings in college for two years after that. I mean of course I came home every summer, but I always went off to camp or to visit relatives with my family. So anyway, I wasn't around long enough to, you know, meet very many people my age.

Still no one had joined them at the empty table which felt like it was growing larger by the minute, so he asked her to dance.

"Sure, I'd love to."

"I have to warn you though, I'm not very good at it. I've only danced a few times before, and had to apologize to the poor girl for stepping on her toes," he said with a self-deprecating grin.

"I promise I won't yell too loudly if you don't yell when I step on yours," she said shyly as she let him guide her onto the dance floor.

"Sounds good to me."

As he danced to the strains of a waltz, he could tell that she'd had formal ballroom training as he had, but long ago in the eighth grade. Though it was fair to say that neither of them showed much enthusiasm. Maybe she had a boyfriend somewhere and was thinking of him. He knew that he couldn't stop thinking of Frances.

After a few miserable dances, Bill and Lucy returned to their table. It was still empty, occupied only by Lucy's evening bag, a lonely little black bag against the snowy white tablecloth.

Bill spent the next few minutes trying desperately to make conversation when he noticed a line forming at the buffet table.

"Why don't we get something to eat?" he suggested.

Lucy's face brightened, and she stood up so quickly, that her chair teetered on its back legs and almost fell over.

At the buffet table, Bill and Lucy took a little of each of the variety of foods offered.

"Does this table go on forever?" Bill asked his date as he looked down the length of the buffet.

"Sure seems that way," Lucy whispered back as she took a small helping of prime rib.

Back at their lonely table, Bill and Lucy ate their dinner and tried to make conversation. Bill looked at his watch more than once and hoped he had not been too obvious. The more he looked at Lucy, the more he thought her a lovely girl, but she wasn't Frances.

When Bill had finished his food, he noticed that Lucy had also finished. "I could go for some more. How about you?" he asked reaching for her plate.

"Yes, thank you." She wiped the corners of her mouth with a dainty motion as Bill swept the plates away, leaving Lucy alone at the table.

As Bill returned with heaping dishes, he happened to notice a young woman on the dance floor whose smile sparkled over the shoulder of her tall, skinny, partner. He stopped dead in his tracks to admire her for a moment, she was so lovely. Her purple gown was decorated with fur at the top of the bodice and at the hemline and it swirled around her graceful form with every dance step. To Bill, it appeared as if she were having more fun than anyone at the party. But the dance floor was so crowded, his view of her lasted only a few fleeting seconds and he made his way back to the table.

As soon as he and Lucy finished eating, he asked Lucy to dance again. He knew he wasn't very good at it, but he had an ulterior motive. He wanted to get a better look at the beautiful girl in the purple gown. As he and Lucy awkwardly made their way around the dance floor, he finally caught sight of her again, but lost her just as quickly. There she was again, but her dance partner was so tall, Bill could only see the top half of her face, but they had made eye contact, and he could have sworn she smiled at him over her partner's shoulder.

She looked vaguely familiar, but in this light and in these unfamiliar surroundings, he couldn't be sure. But he continued to push poor Lucy around the dance floor in hopes of getting a better look at the mystery lady. Finally, it happened, and he could have sworn she looked like Frances.

"Crazy. I'm going crazy," he muttered into Lucy's hair.

"What was that?" she asked looking up at him.

Bill shook his head and smiled down at her. "Nothing. Just talking to myself."

When the music finally stopped, and the girl stepped away from her partner, Bill thought he felt his heart skip a beat. She was Frances!

Now all he could think of was how to get a single dance with her. He couldn't just leave Lucy all by herself. That would be the height of rudeness, but he was quickly becoming desperate. Then he noticed the stag line and thought if he waltzed closer, one of the young men would cut in to free him to ask Frances to dance. But despite his best efforts in that arena, none obliged and he and Lucy returned to their table.

The evening dragged on and instead of looking at Lucy during their halting conversation, his gaze strayed to the dance floor, hoping to catch a glimpse of the love of his life. Then, as if by a miracle, he saw Frances's dance partner head for the men's room. Bill excused himself and quickly followed.

After they'd washed their hands, Bill introduced himself and offered his hand.

"Good to meet you, Bill. I'm Bob."

"Having a good time?" Bill asked.

"Good enough I guess. The food's good at least." He smiled easily.

"I saw you dancing with Frances," Bill commented. "I've been dating her at the university."

"Really. Didn't I see you dancing with Lucy a minute ago?"

"Yes, I was asked to be her escort for the evening. Do you know her?"

"I've known Lucy all my life. Went to elementary school with her before she went off to Virginia."

"And you've known Frances a long time too?"

40

"Heck no. Just met her. I brought her here as a favor to my sister. Frances is a friend of hers and doesn't know anybody else here. Wouldn't you know I'd get stuck with her all night?"

His words gave Bill a brilliant idea. "Bob, listen, maybe I can help you out. Since I happen to be a friend of Frances's, why don't we trade dates? I mean since you know Lucy and I know Frances."

Bob thought a moment. "Well, I don't know. What if the girls object?"

"I don't think Lucy will object. She doesn't know me and I can tell she's having a miserable time with me. And Frances knows me. . . . So what do you say?" Bill asked persuasively.

"Well, if you'll take care of her and see her home, I guess it would be okay. I mean, I don't want my sister getting mad at me about any of this."

"Of course I'll take her home, and you can take Lucy home. You can take care of her for me, okay?"

"Sure. You don't have anything to worry about there."

Bill and Bob shook on their solution and went back to the table where Lucy waited alone. Bob asked her to dance and even though they had barely gotten to know each other, Bill could see she was thrilled. As soon as they left for the dance floor, Bill rushed across the room to Frances.

With his heart pounding louder than the bass drum in the band, Bill approached Frances. "Will you dance with me?"

She looked up at him with her dazzling smile. "Of course I will, Bill, but why did you wait so long?"

"Don't even ask, Frances. I've been having a terrible time. Didn't even recognize you until a few minutes ago. But

41

how come you're here? I thought you were still in Midland?"

She laughed that musical laugh of hers. "My roommate called and invited me. She managed to wrangle an extra invitation to the party, and I uh, was hoping you'd be here. But it made me a little angry to see you dancing with that girl so much. She's so attractive and her dress is absolutely gorgeous, and I think I'm really mad at you about all this, Bill Harris."

Dark as it was, he could have sworn she blushed. Bill couldn't imagine Frances blushing because of him. His eyes must be playing tricks on him.

Then she moved in close, tilted her face up so that it nestled next to his, and rested her hand on the back of his neck. "Dance with me, Bill."

Her whisper sent shivers up and down his spine, his heart pounded faster, and he had the urge to jump up and down for joy, but controlled himself. Instead he pulled her closer and led her onto the dance floor to the strains of "Stardust."

He closed his eyes and imagined himself as a spectator in this scene, he and Frances dancing cheek to cheek. He could hardly believe he held her in his arms. Through their formal evening clothes, he felt the warmth of her body, the softness of her curves, the grace of her movements. And just as he had completely lost himself in the pure sensuality of the moment, his sexuality took over. His arousal clearly began to make itself known and Bill became utterly embarrassed.

Nothing like this had ever happened to him before. What was he going to do? He was thankful for the dimness of the room, perhaps no one would notice. He shifted Frances in his arms so as not to call attention to it, but that would only last

42

as long as the song.

Then suddenly, it seemed as if the room swayed. The lights, the colors, the music all blended together into a cacophony of stimuli. He had no idea what was happening and no idea how to react. Without thinking, he squeezed his eyes shut and hung to on Frances for dear life, hoping for the best. If he was going to die, at least they would be together.

The music and the odd feeling ended at the same moment, and with trepidation, he opened his eyes. The room looked the same. The same people smiled, and danced, and giggled around him. The same band played on the bandstand. The same aromas of food, perfume, and after shave commingled to form a curious but not unpleasant combination. And then he looked down at the girl he held in his arms.

She smiled up at him and the music brightened inside him. The pounding of his heart steadied at a stronger pace. It suddenly seemed that the world was a happier place, colors struck him more vividly, sounds were richer, even the texture of Frances's silk gown slid past his fingers like quicksilver and he knew something had changed. He had fallen in love.

When the strains of "Stardust" came to an end, Bill escorted Frances to the table she had previously shared with Bob. They spent the rest of the evening gazing into each other's eyes, and Bill wondered if Frances felt the same way.

When the band played "Goodnight, Sweetheart," Bill knew the ball had come to a close, and he excused himself to call his father. All the way to her friend's house, they discreetly held hands in the back seat. When they arrived at her friend's house, Bill helped her out of the car and walked her to the door.

"Thank you for a wonderful time, Frances. I don't think I would have made it through the evening if you hadn't been here." He held her hand lightly but desperately wanted to take her into his arms.

"Thank you, too, Bill. I had a lovely time with you."

He bent slightly and placed a chaste goodnight kiss upon her lips, and he congratulated himself for keeping himself in check, particularly with his father glaring at him from the car.

She smiled up at him in response. "Good night, Bill. I'll see you back at school after the holidays," and she let herself into the house.

After the holidays! After the holidays! Holy cow, how long was that? He quickly calculated that wouldn't be for another three weeks or so. Three weeks! How would he make it through the holidays without Frances?

The next morning, Bill saw his picture in the "River Oaks Times" and the photographer had gotten his name exactly right, Bill Harris. He had to chuckle at that, but then his thoughts immediately turned to Frances. He knew she'd be flying home to Midland while he'd remain in Houston. He would cross the days off his calendar at an agonizingly slow pace, until he saw Frances again.

Lovestruck as he was, Bill never thought of calling Frances in Midland. It was, after all, a long distance call, and no matter how much of an emergency he might think it was, he didn't think his mother would share his view. Then he received a letter. Its Midland postmark made him catch his breath. It had to be from Frances.

When he opened it, he took a deep breath of her lingering

fragrance. It was almost as though she were standing next to him. Then he began to read and his heart ached with longing. Her words were sweet and loving. She told him how much she missed him, and how much she wanted to see him. She cared about him. She truly cared about him!

Bill immediately found his stationery and pen and began to write back to her in much the same vein. The words he wrote were for her eyes only. He hoped he could touch her heart in the same way she had touched his. Never very good with words, he labored over each one and made sure they said the things that were in his heart. In a few seconds, the words flowed easily and before he knew it, he had written several pages.

Pleased with his efforts, he slipped his love letter into an envelope, addressed it and made his way to the mail box at the end of his street.

School would not begin again for nearly a month, but now, knowing that she would be waiting for him, he knew he could make it through.

Chapter 5

On the first evening Bill got back to school in mid January, DKE, the fraternity Bill had pledged the previous fall, held its initiation ceremony. He stood with the other five initiates in the darkened living room of the fraternity house, while the chapter president placed a gleaming black and gold pin to his shirt, right above the heart.

"Congratulations, Harris. Now you're officially a DKE. You're one of us." The chapter president shook Bill's hand and gave him a hearty slap on the back.

As soon as the ceremony ended, Bill locked himself in the downstairs bathroom and stared at his image in the mirror over the sink, admiring the way he looked with his fraternity insignia pinned to his shirt. Besides being among the newest members of this brotherhood, the hazing was all behind him now. No more being treated like some kind of galley slave, at least not by his fraternity brothers. After admiring himself for a while he took the pin off and examined it carefully in the light. The pin had spent a few precious minutes in his possession, now he would give it to someone he loved, along with his heart. He quickly ran his fingers through his hair and headed for the Pi Phi sorority house where Frances was waiting for him.

Frances was waiting for him by "their" ping pong table in a well lit, elegantly decorated room, filled with lovely wicker furniture, chintz cushions and memories of their laughter.

"Bill!" she squealed as she ran into his open arms.

"Frances." All shyness gone, he pulled her into his arms and kissed her as he had never kissed her before. Then he held her away from him and looked into her eyes. "You must know I love you. You do know that, don't you, Frances?"

"Bill, oh, Bill, of course I do and you know, you know, oh, I've just missed you so much these past weeks."

"All I want to hear is that you love me as much as I love you. Can you say those words to me?" he asked looking intently into her eyes.

"At least as much, Bill. I love you at least as much as you love me, with all my heart."

Bill released her and reached for the pin still attached to his shirt. "Frances, will you wear my DKE pin? Will you be my love forever?"

Frances stifled the gasp that rose in her throat and clasped her hands to her breast. She nodded and her enormous brown eyes filled with tears as he bent to kiss her. The earth trembled beneath his feet, and he felt as though the whole Pi Phi house would fall down around their heads.

A few evenings later, the entire DKE chapter gathered at the sorority house for the traditional pinning ceremony. One by one, Bill's fraternity brothers arrived and arranged themselves in the yard facing the front of the house. Frances's sorority sisters gathered on the porch and steps of the house while Bill and Frances stood by themselves between the two groups, facing the porch. Finally, a fraternity brother, Charlie

47

Bludworth, sang "Queen of Our Hearts," in his wonderful voice.

As he sang the words, "The girl of my dreams is the sweetest girl the world has ever known. . .," his voice seemed to soar above the heads of the two teenagers, standing love struck and embarrassed among their friends.

When the serenade ended, Bill and Frances shared a long kiss to the enthusiastic whistles and applause of their friends. At that magical moment, Bill realized he didn't want to spend one more second away from this girl than he had to. He wanted to spend every minute of every day with her for the rest of his life. Now all he had to do was figure out how to accomplish that goal.

With the ceremony finished, Bill and Frances went on one of their rambling walks until they found a secluded bench close to the tower. Bill settled himself on the bench and Frances snuggled close. The January cold didn't bother either of them, they were so engrossed in each other, and so much in love. Bill tightened his hold and Frances sighed. When Frances looked up, Bill immediately kissed her, with a longing he had never known before.

When he came up for air, he buried his face in her hair. "Frances," he murmured her name as if it were a prayer. "I know my father will be disappointed, maybe you too, but I'm afraid I'm just not cut out to go into medicine after all."

He stopped, waiting to see her reaction. He prayed she would not be disappointed in him. Instead, all he saw was the sweetness of her smile and the moonlight reflected in her eyes.

"Tell me what you plan instead, Bill."

"I've been thinking about maybe enrolling in the college of education. We could register together tomorrow, if, if. . . ."

"Oh, Bill, that would be wonderful. But your parents. I wouldn't want them to be upset because. . .or think that I...."

Bill stopped their debate with another long kiss.

The next day, he and Frances went through the registration process together. He didn't take the time or the trouble to discuss his change in major from pre-med to education with anyone, particularly not his faculty advisor. He signed up for the same courses that Frances needed for her degree plan. Later they talked about other classes. Bill soon found himself the only male in some of those classes, but he was exactly where he wanted to be, with Frances, and he didn't care one bit.

Because he and Frances shared the same schedule, they spent all day, every day, together. They had the same study period, the same homework, and took the same tests. They even had lunch every day at the same hamburger stand, where the blue plate special was always a quarter hamburger, which was about all they could afford.

Frances had an allowance of $20 a month and Bill's athletic scholarship provided a mere $10 a month for laundry. Bill's mother, however, always included a two dollar bill in her letters to him, which he greatly appreciated. Yet, despite their mutual poverty, they were in love and felt rich in the time they spent together. The only time they spent apart was during Bill's football practice and after curfew when they had to go back to their respective dorms.

The remainder of the winter of 1950 proved mild and the beautiful spring seemed to last forever. Since they had no money to speak of, Bill and Frances found they had a knack for finding fun in ordinary things. All they needed to have a good time was a game of ping-pong or a blanket on the grass around Barton Springs in the sun. And they both discovered they needed a lot of kissing every day.

Occasionally, Bill borrowed a car from his big brother in the fraternity or from some other DKE so they could go out for an inexpensive dinner. Frances had grown up on the banks of the San Marcos River and so loved the water. When the weather grew warm enough, they went swimming. One of Bill's greatest pleasures came when he could hold her in his arms in the water and no one could see what they were doing beneath the surface.

Yet, for all their familiarity with each other, they were both innocents when it came to sex. They had both grown up in sheltered environments and knew virtually nothing about intercourse. Neither knew what "it" was all about, and "how-to" couldn't even be approached. Both were still forbidden topics of conversation in 1950. So they continued to snuggle, and kiss, and stroke each other, but Bill knew that the time would come when he'd have to know more. He didn't want to risk not knowing what to do with Frances.

She might be disappointed. She might get angry. Worse, she might throw his pin in his face and say she never wanted to see him again. He couldn't take the chance, and knew he had to educate himself.

Bill grew more desperate and considered asking one of his fraternity brothers, but thought better of that. It would open him to ridicule. Then he figured he might find his answers in books, so he went to the university library. He hesitated at the door. What was he going to look up anyway? Sex? Intercourse? And how could he maintain his privacy? What if someone should see him reading such a book? He immediately saw that such questions would not get him the information he needed, so he steeled himself and walked inside.

His first inclination was to approach the librarian and ask for her help, but he quickly changed his mind. Instead, he headed for the card catalog and searched for "sex," and came up empty. Then he tried "m" for "man" and "w" for "woman" and still did not find what he wanted. Discouraged, he decided to come back another day.

During the next week, he spent nearly every minute he wasn't with Frances, in the library pulling books from the shelves and checking indexes for some word having to do with sex, but found nothing. He wondered how anybody ever learned how to do anything. Then he noticed an assistant librarian following him and watching his research. Finally, she approached him.

"Excuse me, sir. We, the other librarians and I, couldn't help but notice you in here every day this week. I'm in charge of the Biology section and I'd be more than happy to help with any questions you might have. Can I assist you in finding a particular book?"

Bill felt his face warm and knew he must have turned nine shades of crimson with embarrassment. "Oh, no, ma'am. No thank you, ma'am. I already found what I was looking for. Just checking one last time to be sure there wasn't anything I missed." With that he gave up his quest for book information about sex and fled back to the dormitory, resolved to listen more intently in the locker room.

In the meantime, he and Frances wouldn't change anything about their relationship. They would continue spending time together, kissing, and loving the only way they knew how. Bill only hoped he could learn enough before they got married.

The kissing, however, only got better, and it seemed as if they couldn't be together for more than a few minutes at a time without making lip contact, as happened in their philosophy class.

Philosophy 301 was one of several courses that Bill and Frances had together. Dr. Miller, a visiting instructor from North Carolina, had the honor of teaching 150 student in this class that was held in temporary quarters that looked like a small country church—long and narrow with only one aisle down the center. At the front of the classroom stood an elevated podium and behind that, the obligatory blackboard.

Bill and Frances sat at the back of the class while the professor lectured his students, forty of whom were Bill's fellow football players. There were so many athletes in this class because rumor had it that it was a cinch for at least a B, and Bill needed that B because he was on scholastic probation from the previous semester. He had been enrolled in the school of arts and sciences trying to get into pre-med, but he had neither the interest nor the inclination toward medicine. Frances occupied his mind.

One day in philosophy class, Bill suddenly pulled Frances to him and kissed her. Unfortunately, Dr. Miller saw them.

"I see you two in the back row!" He glared at them. "You can't do that in my class!"

Bill and Frances froze as all heads turned in their direction. They were so embarrassed they couldn't move.

"Just what do you think you're doing? There is a time and place for everything and this is neither the time nor the place!" the professor continued.

Bill looked at Frances and saw that her face had turned a deep red, and knew that if he had a mirror, the color on his face would match.

"Come up here, the two of you," Dr. Miller commanded.

With their gaze fixed on the floor, they moved slowly to the front of the room and they stopped right in front of the professor.

Dr. Miller leaned down over the podium. He lowered his voice to a harsh whisper. "Get your books and coats. You are expelled and will not be allowed to come back."

Gathering what little dignity they had left, they took up their belongings and left the room. By the time they got outside, Frances was in tears.

"It'll be all right, Frances, you'll see," he said helping her on with her coat.

"But he threw us out of class," she said between sobs.

"Now don't cry. You know how I hate to see you cry. Besides, I feel embarrassed and sick enough for both of us."

"But what are we going to do? We both need that class to graduate. You need it to keep your scholarship, and . . . ."

"Shhh. I'll go talk to Dr. Miller. It'll be all right. You'll see," he insisted.

"Do you think you could get him to change his mind?"

"I'll never know unless I try. Right?"

"Right."

He handed her a handkerchief and Frances dried her eyes. Together they waited until the class finished and Bill excused himself to talk to the professor.

Bill couldn't help but notice the profound frown Dr. Miller wore when he approached. "Dr. Miller," he said to catch the instructor's attention.

Dr. Miller stopped in his tracks. "Well, what do you want?"

"I came to apologize and ask you to reconsider," Bill said directly.

"Reconsider? While I'm lecturing, you and your girlfriend are sitting in the back of the room being as rude as two people can be by ignoring me. It's obvious you'd rather do other things with your time than while away your hours in my class." He brought his books up to his chest and hugged them with both arms.

"Please, I'm sorry. We're both sorry. Won't you let us back into your class?"

"If the young lady is so sorry, why isn't she here with you?"

"Because she's embarrassed beyond all belief. Please, Professor," Bill pleaded.

Dr. Miller narrowed his eyes and thought a moment. "You're both suspended for a week. In the meantime, if you want to get back into my class, you'll have to go see the dean."

"Yes, sir. Thank you, sir." Bill felt grateful for even this small reprieve.

Frances wasn't thrilled about the prospect of going to see the dean about getting back into class, but as Bill explained it, neither of them had any choice in the matter.

*   *   *

Dean Parlin was almost seventy years old and about ready to retire. He stood behind his desk, a plump, bald headed grandfatherly man, as Bill and Frances walked into his office. He gestured for them to sit in the chairs in front of his desk.

"Miss Puett. Mr. Harris," he said as he sat in his chair and opened a folder on his desk. He gave it a quick glance before looking up at the couple before him and reading the charges made by Dr. Miller. Then he turned to Frances. "Miss Puett, I believe I know your family. Was your father the Nelson Puett who was quarterback for Texas in 1912?"

He knew her father! Frances didn't know whether to sink into the ground in humiliation or puff up with pride. She only managed a very quiet, "Yes, sir."

"And do you have an older brother who played for Texas in 1938 and scored the winning touchdown against A&M and kept them from going to the Rose Bowl?"

He knew her brother! "Yes, sir." A silent tear slid down her cheek.

The dean turned to Bill. "Now see here, young man. I know this girl's family and I'm holding you responsible for what happened." He paused a moment. "Miss Puett, hold out your hand."

"Yes, sir." Frances did as she was asked.

The dean picked up a 12 inch ruler and whacked Frances on the palm three times, producing more noise than pain.

"Now then, Mr. Harris, hold out your hand."

55

Bill held out his hand and received three whacks to his palm.

Is this it? Bill thought.

Then Dean Parlin held up a 5 x 7 file card and asked Bill, "Do you know what this is?"

"No, sir."

"This is your permanent record card which will be on file forever at the University. I'm writing in green ink that on this date you were reprimanded for being promiscuous in class."

He can't do that! I'll never be able to get a job. I'll be branded as a pervert. But he sat and watched in dismay as the green ink trailed over the white space of his permanent record.

Permanent Record!

The words carried a truckload of dread. It would follow him the rest of his life and he knew the only way he'd ever be able to live it down was to be a model student and citizen from here on out. He couldn't afford to make another mistake.

As soon as their week's suspension was over, he and Frances rejoined their classmates in Philosophy 301. However, they had to apologize to the class and Frances sat in her old seat in the back, while Bill was "encouraged" to take a new seat on the front row.

Chapter 6

As if the turmoil Bill had been through the previous week weren't enough, his mother called that weekend.

"Now don't get excited, Bill, but Dad's in the hospital for some tests."

"Tests for what? What's wrong?" Bill asked. "Is he okay? Are you okay? Listen, I'll take the next bus home."

"Oh, no, dear, don't do that. Not now in the middle of the semester. I'm sure it's nothing but fatigue, all the strain of starting a new practice at his age. Just don't you worry, everything's going to turn out all right I'm sure. I just called because I thought you ought to know."

"But, Mom, I can't just sit here worrying about the two of you. I'd rather be. . . ."

"Now listen to me, son. There's nothing you can do here and you'd be missing your classes. Dad's brothers are right here taking care of things and everything is going to be just fine."

"But, Mom," he continued to protest.

"Please, Bill. Don't make me regret calling you by doing something foolish. Just pray for your father. That's all you need to do to help either one of us."

A few days later, the ring of the hall phone disturbed the

quiet of Hill Hall. Bill pulled the covers over his head and burrowed himself deeper into the blankets. He had decided to sleep in this morning because his first class didn't start until nine. The chill of the early morning air felt good on his face but he preferred the warmth to envelop his body.

The knock on the door further disturbed his sleep but he didn't answer. Another knock elicited a groan.

"Harris!" the voice called from the other side of the door.

Bill immediately reacted to his name. "Yeah. What ya want?" He tried to rub the sleep from his eyes.

"Phone!"

"Who is it?" Bill shouted.

"Sounds like your mother."

The thought of his mother calling him at such an early hour caused him to come instantly awake and he threw the covers from his body.

Jogging down the hall in the dim light of early morning, Bill yawned and adjusted his pajama bottoms around his waist as he made his way to the phone.

"Billy, this is Mother. I'm sorry to call you so early in the day but I had to tell you."

"What's wrong? What's happened to Dad?" Bill began to pace.

"The doctors think he's had a slight stroke, dear."

He felt as if someone had just kicked him in the gut. His breath came in shallow gasps as his mother continued.

"Looking back I think of all those times his eyes would close right in the middle of whatever he was doing. The doctors say they were, well, small strokes, little, tiny ones that had no real impact."

"How is he now?" Bill took a deep breath, expecting the worst.

"He's doing much better now. . . ."

"I'm going to catch the first bus out of here today," Bill said.

"Billy, no. Listen to me. You're father's going to be here a while and he has the best of care, nurses, doctors, medicine, everything he needs. What you can do now is to work hard and pull your grades up. That will cheer your father more than anything once he's in better shape."

"But I need to see him," Bill insisted.

"I know. Listen, the doctors think he can come home in a day or two. But it would mean a lot to him if you'd come home for the weekend, and then you can drive yourself back to school in the other car."

Bill knew she referred to his Dad's 1948 Ford, a little green four door.

His mother's last comment puzzled him. "But won't Dad need the car?"

His mother hesitated a moment. "The doctor doesn't know when Dad will be able to drive again, probably not for a long time. And it wouldn't be good for it to sit there not being used. I have the Oldsmobile that I drive everyday, so I won't be needing the Ford. Besides, it would give you a car on campus, the car would get some use, and you could use it to get home more often."

"Okay, Mother. I'll get a ride home this weekend."

"Thank you, Billy. It'll make your father so happy to see you."

"Sure. See you then." He hung up the phone and slid to

the floor. Numbed by the news, he never felt the cool of the wall against his back or beneath the soles of his bare feet. He drew his legs to his chest and rested his chin on his knees. His father had caused so much pain to his mother and to himself, now he was ill and expected him to run to Houston. But he would go, if for no other reason than to make his mother happy.

Bill found a ride with a fellow football player who was headed home to Houston for the weekend and arrived late Friday night with a load of books and laundry. His mother greeted him at the door.

"Oh, Billy. I'm so glad you're here. Your father will be so happy to see you."

"Is he home?" he asked dropping his bags to the floor.

"Yes, he's upstairs sleeping."

Bill tiptoed up the stairs and carefully he walked down the hall, close to the wall to avoid causing the hardwood floor to creak. Then very slowly, he opened the door to the bedroom that his parents shared, trying to avoid the squeak that always accompanied its movement. He nearly gasped at the sight that greeted him.

He remembered his father as a strapping, dapper gentleman in his early fifties, nearly six feet tall and almost 200 pounds, with a boisterous and sometimes irascible personality, and someone whose laugh boomed through the house. What he saw was the shell of the man beneath the covers of the double bed. His long frame spanned the length of the bed, and his bulk had not diminished so that Bill could tell, but this was not the father he remembered.

The only assurance that the person there still lived was

the barely visible rise and fall of the che... light he could see the paleness of his father's... seemed grayer. The hands seemed older. The che... sunken.

He shook his head and turned to his mother who s... behind him. "I'm tired. I'll see you in the morning." He gave her a peck on the cheek and headed for his room.

Over the next few days, Bill tried to help his mother care for his father, but the only thing he could really do was turn him over when the practical nurse came to bathe him. He tried to help him pass the time by reading aloud from "Texas Football," his father's favorite magazine. However, his father, so usually keen of mind and full of energy, now only barely listened and fell asleep before Bill had read more than a page or two.

By the time Bill got back to school, he was thoroughly depressed and knew he needed something to pick up his spirits. His answer came the next time he saw Frances. Seeing her not only lightened his heart, but her announcement gave him what he needed most.

She hugged him immediately when she saw him. "Bill Harris, where've you been?"

When he told her about his father, her expression immediately turned sympathetic. "I'm sorry to hear that. I knew you had gone home and someone said your father was ill, but I didn't know." She noticed a return of his glum expression. "But I have something that might make you happier," she teased.

Bill cast her a puzzled look.

"Only the biggest winter social event of Pi Phi, our

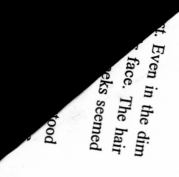

l proudly.

what he needed, but wasn't sure). "I don't know, Frances. I'm not)stume. Especially now, what with

plan our costumes and you'll get 'ore you know it."

thought of her going to the party he wanted so much to spend every moment he could w.... ..er, so he finally agreed that he'd go, but he had no idea as what. A Roman gladiator had some appeal, he thought fleetingly.

For weeks, the Pi Phi's, their friends and dates buzzed with anticipation about the upcoming party. Everyone wanted to know what everyone else was wearing and Bill and Frances came up with dozens of ideas for costumes. They finally settled on attending as a pair of babies.

"I know this seamstress," Frances told him. "She can make us flannel nightgowns, a pink one for me and a blue one for you. She can make us matching mittens and bonnets. We'll be so cute!" she squealed.

The thought of going as a baby had no appeal to him, but he decided to go along with the idea if it made Frances happy. More and more he liked the idea of the gladiator.

As is so often the case in Austin, Texas, no one could have accurately predicted the weather that winter night of 1950. It could have snowed. A hurricane could have rolled in from the Gulf of Mexico. A line of violent thunderstorms complete with hail and tornadoes could have barreled down from the north. Instead, a warm front pregnant with moist, tropical air came up from the south, making it feel more like September than early January.

Bill dressed in his baby costume while his roommate looked on. "You actually paid $10 for that?" He laughed out loud.

Bill shrugged as he looked in the mirror and buttoned the last button at his neck. "It's not that bad. At least it's not a diaper." The simple blue flannel nightgown only came to his knees.

"Good thing it's a warm night," his roommate said with another laugh.

"You got that right. See you later." Bill reached for his keys and wallet and headed out the door.

Bill picked Frances up at Mrs. Bell's Boarding House.

"You look real cute in that," Bill said referring to the pink flannel gown she wore.

Frances giggled. "So do you."

Bill blushed. "I think you look better than I do. Somehow, I don't think these big football player legs look too great with a flannel gown."

"Bill, you'll always look cute to me, no matter what you wear. Come on. Let's go."

When they arrived at the party being held at the Austin's Women's Club, Bill went right to the refreshment table and got them both a glass of punch. When he offered the glass to Frances, he noticed the blush in her cheeks.

"What are you blushing about?" he whispered.

"Well, you know how warm it is tonight?" she said in an equally low voice.

He nodded.

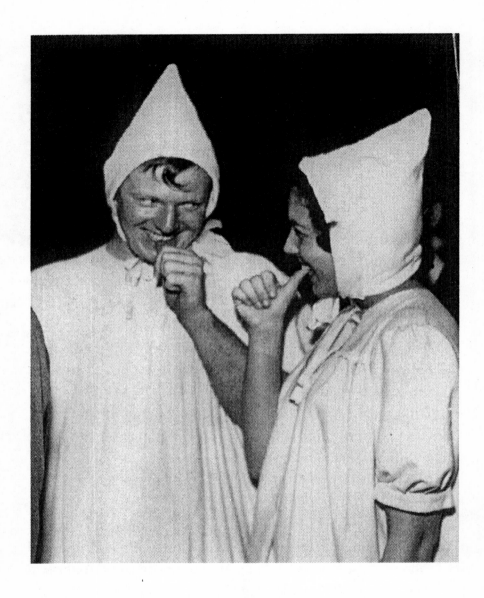

**Bill and Frances in their baby costumes
at the Pi Phi formal costume ball
February 1950**

Bill and Frances at the costume ball.

"I thought it was too warm to wear anything but my underwear underneath the gown," she said shyly.

Bill threw back his head and laughed, then whispered in her ear. "I guess we both thought the same thing. That's all I have on underneath." He raised his punch glass to her and gulped the punch in one swallow.

The party was a huge success. Music filled the rooms, no matter how much people ate or drank, the refreshment table always seemed filled, and Bill and Frances won the contest for the most creative costumes.

As they whirled around the dance floor with several other couples, Bill noticed one of his fellow football players, Earl Fry, a senior, walk into the room.

A hip flask bulged from his pocket and he was barely able to keep his feet. "Come on, everybody! The 'UT Fight Song.' Shing it wiff me."

He began to sing in a less than melodious voice and tried to get others to join in. A friend tried to quiet him but he shook him off. In the next moment, he caught sight of Frances and without a word cut in.

Stunned by such rudeness and arrogance, Bill stood speechless, watching as the drunken student nearly dragged Frances around the floor. Frances, appalled at what had just happened, implored Bill with her eyes to extricate her from this very unpleasant situation.

After a second or two, Bill strode over to the dancing couple.

"You have such beautiful breasts," Earl said staring at her.

Frances's eyes widened in astonishment and then before

66

she could react in any way, Earl reached up with both hands and pinched her nipples. The pain seared through her and she brought her hands to her breast in a protective gesture while tears sprang to her eyes.

Without thinking, Bill doubled his right hand into a fist and swung at the football player's chin as hard as he could. He wobbled on his feet for a second or two before falling to the floor in a heap.

Bill grabbed Frances's hand. "Quick, let's get out of here before he wakes up and kills me."

He didn't have to tell her twice. Frances was more than willing to leave and they ran from the building, got into the car, and drove off into the night.

Frances sobbed in shame and held her hands over her breasts. Bill reached over and drew her closer. Draping his arm across her shoulders he tried to comfort her and wished he could comfort himself as well. Thoughts of what that senior would do to him tomorrow sent shivers through him. Lord, he would beat him to a pulp!

"I can't go back to the boarding house tonight, not after this. I'm just so embarrassed, Bill."

"You didn't plan to go back there anyway tonight, did you?"

"You're right. I asked Katy if I could spend the night with her tonight so I wouldn't have to make the 12:30 curfew at Mrs. Bell's."

"What will she think when you don't show up?" Bill asked.

"She'll just think I changed my mind and went back to the house." Then she looked at Bill. "What did you have in mind?"

He smiled down at her. "Trust me."

Frances snuggled closer and wiped the tears from her cheeks.

Mount Bonnell, the highest point in Austin, overlooked the city with its grid of twinkling lights. As the midnight hour approached, Bill and Frances watched from the car as little by little the lights winked out and Bill and Frances watched from a secluded spot under a tree. The moon shone on the Colorado River like a shimmering ribbon and Bill took his beloved in his arms.

"It'll be all right, Frances. By tomorrow, no one will ever remember what happened." He only hoped the guy he decked wouldn't remember.

"Oh, Bill, that awful boy hurt me when he did that." She hugged herself and shivered.

Bill held her as tight as he could and Frances tucked her head under his chin as she whimpered.

"It's okay, Baby. It's all right, Frances." He rocked her gently in his arms. He found the smell of her hair intoxicating and kissed the top of her head. "I love you, Frances. I'll protect you. I'll protect you for all our lives if you'll let me."

Surprised at his confession, she looked up at him. Bill lowered his face to hers and kissed her lips, gently, tenderly at first, and then becoming more ardent as the seconds passed. Seconds turned into minutes and the windows fogged with heat from their bodies.

Finally, Frances broke from the embrace. "Bill, you've got to put the windows down. It's so hot in here I think I'm going to melt."

"It's these damn itchy flannel gowns, Frances. I think I'll die if I don't get out of mine." He held her away from him and looked down into her face in the moonlit darkness. "We could take them off, you know."

Frances felt herself warm at the suggestion. "It really wouldn't be any different than when we're in bathing suits, would it, Bill?"

He nodded in numb agreement.

"And it still hurts where he pinched me." She added the final justification.

Bill took a deep breath and struggled out of his long, sweaty costume, which by now was wrapped around him like a steaming blanket. Free of the flannel, he began kissing Frances on the mouth, then made a trail of kisses to her neck, then found his way lower to her breasts through the fabric of the gown. Gently, he tugged it out from under her and lifted it over her head.

Frances felt the sodden flannel trail over her body and a shiver of delight traveled through her. For the first time ever, a man held her as she sat clad only in her bra and panties. Doubts filled her mind.

Nice girls don't do things like this.

Nice girls don't let boys get too familiar.

Nice girls. . .nice girls. . .nice girls.

But it felt so right, here in Bill's arms and she melded into his body.

He held her beautiful breasts in his hands and tenderly kissed them, ever mindful of her truly bruised and sore nipples. He made a necklace of kisses at her throat, ran his hands down her back. Frances had never felt anything so delicious and it made her shiver with pleasure. But their loving stopped there.

Bill knew he loved her, but she didn't belong to him. They had no commitment. They had no real plans. And they certainly were innocent of anything more. In truth, neither of them would have known exactly what to do. Instead, they spent the rest of the night in the car, snuggled close together for comfort and warmth as the night grew cooler. All thoughts of what he might face the next day had left him. The only thing he knew, the only thing that was important to him, was the beautiful young woman he held in his arms and the happiness he found with her.

She slept in his arms until fist light when he drove her to Katy's house, the friend who had expected her earlier.

The next day, Bill gave Earl a wide berth whenever he saw him, but he soon found out it hadn't been necessary. He had such a hangover, he wouldn't have cared if Mount Bonnell had come crashing in on him. Besides, Bill also learned that Earl had no memory of anything that had happened at the party, and no one had stepped forward to fill him in. Bill breathed a bit easier knowing that Earl was not going to try to even the score with him for knocking him out cold.

Able to relax a little, all fear gone of being pummeled into the ground, Bill looked back on his night with Frances as though he had spent the night with an angel. She had been warm, and lovely, and vulnerable in his arms, and he had been her knight in shining armor. He would love her forever. He only hoped she felt the same way about him.

Chapter 7

Whether fall or spring, the UT campus buzzed with activity. Football was the big sport in the fall and basketball reigned in the spring. In addition, clubs, sororities, and fraternities sponsored a variety of functions. One weekend it might be the Varsity Carnival or float building for the upcoming Round Up Parade. Of course there were the Texas Relays, house parties at the coast, and dozens of ways to have fun in and around Austin. And the DKEs enjoyed a great weekend in Wimberley at the place called the Eagles Nest Guest Ranch.

As the weeks wore on, each day grew warmer than the one before. The days lengthened and the sun shone brighter. Bill and Frances took advantage of the beautiful weather and went swimming as often as they could. Sometimes they went swimming at Barton Springs or Lake Austin. Sometimes they rented inner tubes for a quarter each at Camp Wernecke in New Braunfels so they could ride the rapids. They'd put their tubes in the water way upriver and enjoy leisurely floats back down to the rapids then do it over and over again until it got dark.

Another one of their fun activities was to go to San Marcos where there was a lake with a huge wooden tower to dive from. Neither considered themselves a great diver, but the tower had three levels you could dive from plus a steel cable that started at the very top of the tower and extended out and down to the middle of the lake. A small wooden hand cart with a handle hung from the cable so anyone who wanted, could push off from the top platform and ride the hand cart out to the middle of the water.

One time, while they were there, Bill nudged Frances and pointed to the slide. "Why don't we give that a try?"

Frances took a long hard look at the slide, the cart, and the middle of the lake. "I don't know, Bill. It doesn't look too safe."

"So what if it's not. You'll only fall into the water, the place where you were heading anyway."

She shook her head. "But it's so high at the top. I don't think so." She nervously checked that the straps of her white swim suit were still tucked into the top part of her suit.

"Look, everybody is having a great time. It's certainly strong enough to handle those big guys."

Frances gave the slide a long, studied look.

"Listen, I'll go first and wait in the water in case you have any trouble. Okay?"

Frances hesitated and finally mumbled her agreement.

Together they climbed the tower. At the top, Bill grabbed hold of the handle and kicked off. "Geronimo!" he yelled as he slid down and sliced into the water.

Frances watched carefully and finally expelled her breath when Bill's head bobbed to the surface. He wore a huge smile. "It's fun! Come on in," he shouted and waved as he tread water.

Frances pulled on the cord that worked as a pulley which brought the cart back to the top of the tower. With sweaty palms, Frances seized the handle, her knuckles showing white. She followed Bill's example and pushed off the platform. The moment she swung out on the cable with her arms fully extended above her head, the bodice of her suit dropped, exposing her breasts and part of her stomach. She was mortified and wanted to drop into the water immediately, but she was still far too high to let go, and there was no way she could hold on with just one hand and pull her suit up with the other. Frustrated and humiliated, Frances screamed the whole way down, which of course drew the attention of the crowd.

Bill didn't know what to do. Should he look or not?

He looked.

It was the first time, in full daylight, he saw how truly beautiful Frances's body was, and he could do nothing but stare. In another second, she hit the water and Bill swam over to her.

When she came to the surface, she was sobbing and trying to pull up her suit while treading water. "Why do these things happen to me?" she whispered between sobs.

He helped her pull the top of her suit up and tied the straps securely behind her neck, then tried to comfort her. He wanted to tell her that maybe subconsciously she wanted her suit to fall because she knew she had the best figure around, but thought better of it. Instead, he held her and tried to blend in with the crowd. Finally, he had her laughing and giggling about it and assured her that was so high up, no one could ever be sure who the Lady Godiva of the cable ride had really been.

But swimming didn't occupy all their time together. They enjoyed Austin's Bull Creek Park as a postcard perfect place with its boulder strewn creek as the centerpiece. Bill and Frances often went to the park with a large group of friends, mostly Bill's pledge brothers and their girlfriends, for an afternoon picnic, softball game, and then a cool down in the creek. Life was wonderful and Bill was the happiest he had ever been in his life and he hoped his happiness would continue indefinitely.

He and Frances never talked about marriage, but it was something that they both took for granted, knowing that it would happen for them, someday, as soon as possible. Because they were both thinking along the same lines, they had a great time together shopping in the basement of Scarborough's department store buying things for their first apartment. In a few weeks, they had bought several of the discounted, discontinued items. A little four-cup coffee pot caught Frances's eye, along with some cheap, plastic dishes called Mellowear. They found a setting for four of stainless steel flatware and a few other inexpensive things they thought they'd need for their first kitchen. And they kept everything they'd bought in the trunk of Bill's dad's car. . .unopened.

Bill and Frances in 1950. They look so happy together.

Chapter 8

By now, Bill knew for certain that he was in love with Frances and wanted to spend the rest of his life with her. But all this time that he'd been seeing her, the only time they had spent alone together had been severely limited. They had almost always been together in public, or under the watchful eye of an adult. He had to come up with a plan.

He wanted to spend some time alone with Frances in his room, and the University was very strict about things like that. In fact, it was unheard of, and grounds for dismissal if you got caught. But there had to be a way to accomplish his goal. After thinking about it for a few days, an idea struck him, but it hinged on his roommate and how much Frances trusted him.

Dick Austin, Bill's roommate came back to the room one late Wednesday afternoon. He dropped his tennis racket and the rest of his gear on his bed and began gathering his things for the shower.

Bill looked up from his book and waited for the right moment. "So how was practice today?"

"Great. If we play at the tournament like we played today, we'll win our match next week," Dick said pulling a towel from the rack.

"So your match is next week? Not this weekend?" Bill asked.

"Yes, next week. This weekend I'm going to Denton to see my girl. You know I go up to see her once a month. Why?" Dick wanted to know.

"Nothing. I just wasn't sure if it was this weekend or next weekend." Bill didn't dare tell his roommate what he had in mind. The less he knew the better all the way around. If he got caught, he didn't want to jeopardize Dick.

Dick cast him a curious look and headed for the bathroom. With a sense of anticipation, Bill began working the plan that would get Frances up to his room. The first thing he did was to call Frances and ask her if he could see her on Saturday night.

"Bill, I'd love to. What did you have in mind?" she asked.

"It's a surprise," was all he told her.

Now all he had to do was wait for Dick to leave, and leave he did, first thing that Saturday morning.

"See you on Sunday night," Dick said as he headed for the door.

Bill waved. "Have a safe trip and say hello to your girl for me."

That afternoon, Bill went downtown to the basement of Scarborough's department store and bought the biggest laundry bag they had, one they called a "duffle bag." He took it to his room and filled it with dirty laundry and shoved it into the corner of his room. He looked at his watch and saw that it was only 4:00. He had told Frances he'd pick her up about 6:00.

Bill needed something to do to fill the time, so he had dinner and did some homework. Finally, when he thought he could stand it no longer, Bill noted the time at 5:45. With a spring in his step, he hoisted the stuffed laundry bag over his shoulder and headed to Mrs. Bell's boarding house. When Frances saw him with the bag over his shoulder, she gave him a certifiably puzzled look.

"So are you supposed to be Santa Claus?" She tried to stifle her laughter but a giggle escaped.

"No," he answered coyly.

"I know. Let me guess. This is the surprise. You want me to do your laundry! Right?"

"No, just come with me and you'll see real soon."

Frances followed Bill from the boarding house as they walked toward the University and in the direction of the athletic dorm where Bill lived. Bill looked all around to make sure no one was around.

When he pulled her behind a huge live oak tree, Frances finally asked, "Bill, what is wrong with you?"

"Shhh." He dumped the laundry on the ground and held it open. "Get in."

"What? Get in?" She looked at him as though he were crazy but Bill pretended not to notice.

"Honey, please just get in the bag," he pleaded.

She looked at him like he'd lost his mind and started backing away. "What did you say, Bill?"

"Please, sweetheart, just get in the bag."

"But I don't understand. Why in the world would you ask me to do something like that?"

He lowered his voice to a whisper. "Listen, Frances, Dick

has left for the weekend which means I'm alone this weekend. This is a chance for us to be together, in private. Now please just get in the bag."

Frances shook her head and muttered. "I don't know which one of us is crazier." She stepped into the bag and Bill pulled it up over her head.

"Get down," he said.

After she crouched as far down as she could, he stuffed the laundry in all around her so nothing of her shape showed through. He tied the rope securely at the top of the bag then threw it over his shoulder and headed for the front door of his dorm.

Frances grew more nervous by the second. She was hot and having difficulty breathing. Bill, hearing her in the bag whispered for her to be quiet.

"Quiet?" she whispered back. "I'm trying to stay alive in here."

"We're almost there now. In fact, we're getting ready to go in the front door, so be still. I'm sure a bunch of the guys are in the lobby."

The moment he opened the door, he saw that he had been right.

"Hey, Harris, what have you got there?" one of his friends asked.

Bill never lost his stride. "Damn month's worth of laundry is all." He sounded as grouchy as he knew how as he headed for the stairs.

"Brother, he's in a mood," he heard one of the guys say as he began his ascent.

Once on the second floor, he hurried down the hall to his

room, ran through the door and locked it behind him. He quickly opened the bag and Frances stumbled out with a dirty tee shirt hanging off one shoulder and collapsed onto the bed. "What an insane idea. You're out of your mind, and I'm as crazy as you are for going along with it."

Bill sat beside her and embraced her. Frances only glared at him then jumped up and stalked across the room to the tiny bathroom. He started to follow until he heard the door slam, and when he heard the tumblers on the lock click into place, stopped dead in his tracks.

The idea suddenly seemed a dismal failure. Sure, he had snuck her into his room, but at what cost? For certain Frances thought of him as a complete lunatic now. He wouldn't blame her for ever refusing to see him again. He wouldn't blame her for throwing his pin back in his face. He moved closer to the door.

"Frances, I'm sorry. I thought it was a good idea at the time," he said quietly through the door.

Silence.

"Frances, please talk to me."

Silence.

He didn't know what to do. He had thought this was a wonderful idea. He had been utterly wrong. Bill sank to the bed. Looking at the crumpled heap of dirty laundry and empty laundry bag, he had to admit it seemed like a good idea at the time, but now he wasn't so sure. His desire to spend time alone with Frances had led him to a desperate action. Without any idea what to do next, Frances helped him decide.

She emerged from the bathroom, and leaning against the doorjamb folded her arms over her chest.

Bill didn't say a word, he only stood to face her, determined to let her set the tone of what would follow.

Without hesitation, she walked over to him, put her arms around his neck and nestled her head against his chest. "My clothes reek of some old football player's dirty laundry. I hope you don't mind if I get this close." She looked up at him with a broad smile.

Her actions and attitude took Bill completely off guard. "I d. . .don't m. . .m. . .mind at all," he managed to stutter until Frances stood on tiptoe to give him a kiss.

In a few minutes, they had pushed the two beds together and lay side by side. Pulling Frances close to him, he noted every curve of her warmth as he held her. He filled himself with her fragrance. He traced the curve of her jaw with the tip of his finger. "You feel like silk," he whispered in her ear.

Frances blushed and stroked the tiny hairs at the back of his neck. "I like the way you feel too, Bill."

Bill and Frances kissed and snuggled close to each other, feeling the heat of each other's bodies through their clothes.

Finally, Frances sat up on the bed and looked at the alarm clock on Bill's nightstand. "Bill, look, it's getting late."

"I'd better get you back," he said sadly.

She cupped his face in her palm. "Don't look so sad, Bill. We had a wonderful time together. At least I did."

"Oh, I did too," he quickly broke in. "It's just that I hate to see it come to an end so soon."

She smiled at him. "We'll have a lifetime together. This was just the beginning."

The thought of spending a lifetime with Frances was enough to send him into a tailspin. What a wonderful thought.

With a deep breath, Frances got back into the bag and allowed Bill to stuff his dirty laundry on top of her once again. He retraced his steps down the hall, down the steps, and out the front door. It was a Saturday night, so they encountered very few people in the lobby. When he found a secluded spot behind a nearby tree, Bill stopped and let Frances out of the bag.

She took a deep breath of fresh air when she stepped out of the bag. "Well, that was an adventure." She stood on tiptoe and gave him a sweet kiss.

"So you're not angry?" he asked.

"Not overly much." She smiled at him.

Bill walked her back to Mrs. Bell's then came back to the oak tree to recover his clothes. It was one of the happiest days of his life. This girl he loved was gorgeous and perfect and he wanted her more than anything in the world. Someday, some way it would be right for them to be together, of that he had no doubt.

Chapter 9

As the semester wound down, the weather grew warmer and spring football came to a close. Bill and Frances made a concerted effort to do some serious studying in preparation for finals. For two weeks before the much anticipated exams, they studied together just about every night in the library.

Then the Sunday just before finals, Bill and Frances bumped into a friend after the 8:00 church service. Mary Jo was one of Frances's sorority sisters and a graduate student. She was dating Albert, one of Bill's senior fraternity brothers.

"Frances and Bill!" Mary Jo greeted them with big hugs just outside the church.

"I didn't see you in the church," Frances said.

"I got here just a minute before the service began so sat way in the back. I didn't want to disturb anyone. So are you two ready for finals?"

"We've been studying hard," Bill said.

"Boy have we ever. Bill and I have our own special corner of the library where we've been cracking the books for two weeks now."

Mary Jo nodded. "I know what you mean. Albert and I have been putting in lots of study hours too. Listen, I don't know about you two, but we've had just about all the studying we can stand for now. Albert and I have decided to go to the coast for the day and relax on the beach. Why don't you two join us?"

Bill and Frances looked at each other.

"Do you think we've studied enough?" Frances asked.

A broad grin spread across Bill's features. "I think we can knock off for one day. What do you say? Shall we go?"

Frances smiled and nodded.

"Great!" Mary Jo squealed. "You two go get your suits and meet us back here at my car and we'll spend the day at Galveston."

A single day of relaxation seemed a reasonable thing to ask before the ordeal of exams began and so Bill and Frances rushed back to their dorms for their suits. They climbed in the back seat of Mary Jo's car and the four of them began the four-hour trip to Galveston.

The arrived at Stewart Beach a little after one that afternoon and spent the next few hours swimming and having fun in the water. By five that afternoon they were tired and sunburned and decided they should get back since the girls had to be in by 10:30.

They piled into the car, wet towels and all, and Mary Jo drove them away from the beach. Bill and Frances had been sitting in the back seat, and after several hours, had drifted off to sleep. A terrible crash jolted him and then silence.

When Bill awoke, he was hanging halfway over into the front seat. Sleep had muddled his brain and he wasn't thinking clearly at first. When he looked to his right, where Albert should have been sitting, he thought he saw a pile of rags. When he took a second look, he saw that it was Frances, slumped like a feather pillow against the front door frame.

He shook the sleep from his head and took a second look around him. The car wasn't moving and the door on the driver's side was wide open. Blood was everywhere.

He saw Frances. "You all right?" Bill managed to croak.

She didn't answer.

"There's been an accident. Are you all right? Are you hurt?"

She moaned again. "I don't know. Yes. No. I'm. . . . But where are we?" She suddenly realized she was sitting in the front passenger seat. "But how did I get up here? Where's Mary Jo?" She screamed and pointed. "Bill, Albert's out there on the hood. He's gone through the windshield, and he looks like, oh, my God, Bill. He looks like he's dead."

Bill looked through the windshield on his side and saw the hood of another car melded to their driver's side hood. They'd been hit head on with full force by another car.

Frances worked the handle of the passenger side door trying to get it open but couldn't get it to budge. Bill forced open the back door and fell to his knees beside Mary Jo, another sight that would stay with him for a long time.

Mary Jo lay sprawled on the highway in a bed of splintered glass. Blood bubbled up out of her arm, from her face, her neck. He looked around for something to use as a compress, a tourniquet, anything, but could find nothing useful at hand.

"I can't get out," Frances screamed in panic. "The door won't open. I've got to get out of here!"

He turned his attention to Frances and called to her. "Crawl over the seat and come out the back door. Come out this way, Frances."

Her breath came in huge, heaving sobs but she climbed over the seat while Bill went back to Mary Jo. Frances went to see if she could do anything for Albert.

"Albert's cut to pieces," she screamed.

"Mary Jo's pretty bad too. We've got to get help." Bill looked up to see her dive into the back seat and begin rummaging through their things on the floor.

"Towels. We need towels. Where are our towels?" Finally, she grabbed something and threw it in Bill's direction. "Use that one for Mary Jo." She took another and went to Albert.

By the time he'd finished doing what he could for Mary Jo, Frances has come up beside him. "Is she. . .will she be okay?"

Bill shook his head. "I don't know."

Frances reached for the towel. "Here, Bill, let me take care of her. You go see about the people in the other car."

Just then another set of headlights topped a small rise in the road coming from LaGrange. He glanced inside the car they'd hit to see two bodies overlapping one another across the front seat.

Bill tore his blood stained tee shirt from his body and ran out to the middle of the road. The car screeched to a stop.

"Please go back to LaGrange and get them to send an ambulance as fast as they can. These people are hurt pretty bad," he shouted at the startled man inside the car.

The driver nodded once, then backed down the highway far enough to turn around and head back the way he'd come. Meanwhile, Frances had moved to the far side of the car they'd hit. Leaning inside through the passenger side window, she held a towel to what appeared to be someone's forehead.

With one eye on the road, Bill went to check on Mary Jo again. She hadn't lost nearly as much blood as Albert but was still out cold. When he'd done what he could, which was very little except to beg God to let her be all right, he peered up and down the road looking for other cars, but saw not a single light, not even from a farm house. What he did see was the telltale evidence of the accident on the highway.

A set of skid marks painted a grim picture of a head-on collision. Mary Jo's car had crossed over into the left lane and hit an oncoming car, a Buick, that must have been traveling at least sixty miles an hour. He shook his head and wondered how he and Frances had survived it so well.

He turned his attention back to Albert and saw that fresh blood had already soaked the towels on his face. Bill knew that Frances had already used their other towels on the occupants of the other car.

He hadn't heard anything from her in minutes, but as he walked back to the other car, a second set of headlights came at him from the direction of LaGrange. Again he waved his shirt in the glare of the headlights.

"Please go for the sheriff," Bill pleaded with the driver.

Little more than a boy, the driver stared at the scene of twisted metal and bloody bodies without responding to Bill's request.

"Can you hear me?" Bill asked.

The boy nodded numbly, mesmerized by the bloody scene before him.

"You've got to get the sheriff," Bill repeated. "And get an

ambulance. We have people here who are hurt. They need medical help."

Suddenly, he "came to" and with an abrupt nod, turned the car around.

After what seemed like hours of taking care of four unconscious and severely injured people, the ambulance and sheriff finally arrived and took control of the situation. The medical people began loading the injured people while the sheriff investigated the crash scene.

"No, no one was drinking."

"No, they didn't see anything."

"We were asleep in the back seat."

"It had already happened when we woke up."

"No, we didn't hear anything until it was all over."

Even if we had been awake, we probably wouldn't have seen much. It had happened about 9 p.m., well after dark, and there were no street lights on that country road.

Their answers had disappointed the sheriff, but he could see the skid marks left by one car and he took notes on his clipboard while Bill and Frances leaned against the sheriff's vehicle, still shaken from the ordeal.

"So you two sure you're not hurt?" the sheriff asked again.

"I don't think so," Bill answered for the both of them.

"Well, you've got enough blood on you for all four of these people, but I'm glad you two at least seem to have escaped injury. Even so, get in the car, I'll take you to the hospital to get checked out."

The ambulance beat the sheriff to the hospital by a matter of minutes and when he arrived with Bill and Frances, the ambulance driver and medical technicians were already unloading their human cargo. Bill and Frances followed the sheriff into the emergency room and he told them to take a seat.

Chapter 10

Because it was late on a Sunday, only one doctor remained on duty, and the few nurses who were also on duty, scrambled to determine the most severely injured. Bill and Frances watched, wide-eyed as the small, efficient staff directed the emergency medical technicians to take the injured into a curtained area behind the desk.

"Doctor," the sheriff said approaching the lone doctor. "These two young people were also in the accident. They say they're all right, but I've seen enough of these accidents to know they should be checked out."

The doctor nodded. "Right, Sheriff. Soon as we're done taking care of these other people. They look like they need immediate attention." He nodded in the direction of Bill and Frances. "We'll get to them soon."

Just before he turned to go, Frances called to him. "Doctor, are they going to be all right?"

"Friends of yours?" he asked.

She nodded.

"We'll see. I'll let you know as soon as I can." He turned on his heel and headed for the curtained area.

"Okay, you two. You heard the doctor. He'll be with you

as soon as he can. In the meantime, let's see if you can remember anything else about the accident."

The doctor and his staff worked on the two people who had been in the other car first because they were more severely injured. In the meantime, Mary Jo and Albert lay on gurneys in the hall, only feet from where Bill and Frances stood talking to the sheriff.

They only repeated what they had already told him, that they had fallen asleep on the way back from Galveston and when they woke up, it was all over.

Just then, the doctor came to work on Mary Jo and Albert. As he gave them a quick exam, Bill crept up beside him. "How does it look?" he asked.

The doctor gave Bill a quick glance and then got back to his work. "The young lady has lacerations and bruises to her face and neck." His hands deftly moved to her neck. "Possible broken collar bone, and the young man has severe lacerations to his face and head. They've both lost a lot of blood, but I think they're going to pull through." He turned to an orderly. "Take them down to x-ray."

The doctor eventually came back out to examine Bill and Frances and confirmed their assessment that they were uninjured.

"So, where can I drop you?" the sheriff asked after the doctor had released them.

Bill reached into his pocket and pulled out two dollar bills. "I don't know. I don't suppose we could get back to the University on this."

"You're right there, young man. Let me take you someplace for the night and you can call friends and family in

91

the morning. It's too late to do anything now."

The sheriff took them to the LaGrange Hotel and paid for two single rooms next to each other. They thanked him for his kindness and went to their rooms. Bill headed for the shower.

The hot water flowing over his body, washing away the dirt and grim and blood of these past few hours felt wonderful. It was as if he could wash it all down the drain. He never wanted the warmth or the clean feel of the water to end. But he finally shut the water off and reaching for the towel, stepped out of the tub. A sound caught his attention. He paused a moment to listen. He could hear Frances sobbing on the other side of the wall. His heart broke for her and he placed his hand on the wall, almost as if hoping to reach through to touch her.

Quickly, he dressed and rushed to her door and knocked. No answer came.

"Frances, open up." He listened but she hadn't heard him. All he heard was the sound of her sobs.

He banged on the door. "Frances!"

Finally, she came to the door and inched it open. That small opening was all that Bill needed and he moved inside the little room. She fell into his arms and let her tears fall upon his shoulder.

Gently he guided her over to the bed where they sat together in a close embrace while Frances cried her eyes out and Bill's heart broke for her.

"It was horrible, Bill. I never saw anything so horrible in my life."

"Shhh. They're all going to be okay. Don't worry about it now."

"But the blood, the car, the. . . ."

He quieted her with a kiss. "Come on. It's all going to be all right. Why don't you lie down and go to sleep?" he suggested. "You look exhausted."

She shook her head. "I can't. Every time I close my eyes I see Albert lying across the hood of that car." She shivered. "I see Mary Jo sprawled out on the highway, all cut up and bleeding everywhere. I don't think I can ever go to sleep again."

"Now you know that's not so," he said as though trying to comfort a little child awakened by a terrible nightmare. "It's all over with now. They're going to be all right. We're fine. We walked away without a scratch. But you need to rest."

She nodded. "You're right, of course."

Bill helped her up from the bed and then pulled down the covers for her. Obediently, Frances slipped into bed while Bill pulled the blankets up over her.

"I'll see you in the morning."

Frances grabbed for his arm. "No, Bill. Don't leave me. I don't think I could spend the night alone."

With a sigh, Bill nodded. "Okay. I'll stay." He lay next to her, atop the covers. The warmth of the May night came in at them from the open window and washed over them. Bill held her in his arms until she fell asleep, then moved back to his own nightmarish dreams of the day's events and returned to his room.

Early the next morning, Bill called the hospital to check on his friends. The duty nurse assured him that both Mary Jo and Albert would be fine and that their parents were on the way. Frances felt much better when he gave her the news. Then he called his roommate, Dick Austin.

"Dick, this is Bill."

"Where've you been?" his roommate asked excitedly. "You were missing when they did bed check and I didn't know what to say. Are you all right?"

"I'm fine. I'm with Frances."

Dick whistled. "Mrs. Bell must be going crazy with worry over at the boarding house."

The curfew had never occurred to him, and he was sure it has slipped Frances's mind as well. It was difficult to think about something as trivial as a curfew when life and death hung in the balance.

"Listen, Dick. We're at a hotel in LaGrange. . . ."

"A hotel?"

"Please, can you come pick us up? I'll tell you all about it when you get here." Bill gave him the name of the hotel and directions to get there.

"All right. Sit tight. I'm on my way."

When Bill hung up the phone, he told Frances about his curfew concerns.

Her hands flew to her face. "Oh, my God, Bill. What's going to happen? We both missed curfew. I'm sure by now Mrs. Bell has called my parents, the dean, my friends! And what about you?" With a sickening feeling she sank to the bed.

"Don't worry Frances. When we tell them what happened, I'm sure everyone will understand. There was a terrible accident and people almost died. We were lucky to walk away. We did the best we could under terrible circumstances. I don't think anyone can hold that against us. Besides, nothing happened. We didn't do anything wrong." He sat beside her and draped his arm across her shoulder.

Frances shuddered. "I hope you're right."

"Come on. Let's see what we can get for breakfast for two bucks. Dick should be here in an hour or so."

Chapter 11

Bill and Frances arrived back at their dorms that Monday afternoon and were called in by the deans of men and women, Dean Dorothy Gebauer and Dean Jack Holland. They each scolded us and informed us of the university rules we had broken:

1. failure to obtain written parental permission to go out of town.
2. failure to sign out before leaving the city limits of Austin.
3. failure to return by 10:30.
4. failure to notify our house mothers.

Bill tried to explain. "We didn't know where we were going exactly until we got to Galveston, and had no thought of staying out past curfew. We just went swimming with a couple of friends and not one of us had a drop of alcohol to drink.

"It was a long and tiring day and we fell asleep on the way home. Finally, Mary Jo, the driver fell asleep on the way home and that caused the accident. We were all nearly killed! Frances and I were so lucky and it was a miracle we weren't seriously injured. We didn't intentionally do anything wrong.

It was all innocent and a terrible accident!

"By the time the sheriff came, it was late on Sunday night and we didn't have anywhere to go. The Sheriff was kind enough to take us someplace where we could spend the night, and he paid for both rooms out of his own pocket. He never even asked for any money back. We didn't do anything wrong."

The dean only glared at him.

"Maybe I didn't do exactly as everyone would have expected me to do, but I did the best I could, and none of it was wrong," Bill concluded.

"You're right, Mr. Harris. You exhibited poor judgment. You should have called the University as soon as you could to explain the situation. I'm sure we would have sent someone for you, no matter what time it was. At best, it was improper for the two of you to spend the night at the hotel, even if you did have separate rooms. At worst, it looks as though you've done something downright immoral. You say you did nothing wrong, and I'm inclined to believe you, particularly since I know Ms. Puett's family. However, we can't let this pass as though nothing has happened."

Bill held his breath, as though waiting for the guillotine to fall across his neck.

"You are placed on social probation and I'm going to call your parents to tell them what happened. Since final exams have started, I will let you take them and *not* send you home in disgrace."

With a sigh of relief, Bill thanked the dean for his understanding and left the office.

Bill left for his dorm to rest and get ready for his second

final at 9 a.m. on Tuesday.

Early the next morning, as Frances was getting ready to leave for her exam, she received a phone call.

"Frances, this is the president of Texas Alpha Sorority. Be here at 10 o'clock to appear before a joint meeting of the Pi Phi Mother's Club and the Austin Alumni Club, and bring Bill with you."

She suddenly felt as if her stomach had twisted itself into a knot. "But I have exams to take," she protested.

"That does not matter to us."

"But we've already talked to the dean about this. I thought it was all straightened out with the University."

"Maybe it is. . .with the University. But you still have to reckon with us," and she hung up the phone.

Frances stood there for a long moment listening to her heart hammer in her chest. What would they do to her? Lord, she hoped they wouldn't expel her from the sorority. What a disgrace! Her mother, Honey Harwood, had been a member of that sorority. What would she do?

As a strange coincidence, Bill's mother, Almeida McGregor had also been a member of Pi Phi and had been friends with Honey in 1918.

Tears began to wend their way down her cheek. She wiped them away with the back of her hand, took a deep breath, and looked at her watch. She still had time to make her nine o'clock exam.

Across campus at Hill Hall, Bill received the same phone call.

"But we've met with the dean already," Bill said reiterating what Frances had said.

"As I said to your 'friend,' we don't care. That's how the

My Dear _____,

I have returned from New York and Billy has told me of
the unfortunate trip to Galveston and the car accident that occurred
on the way back to Austin. Honestely, it has taken several days for
me to recover from the shock of it all—words never seemed so
empty, but I want you and Nelson to know how deeply grieved I
am that my boy could <u>ever</u> have permitted Frances to go on such a
trip. I'm grateful it was no worse, but heart broken that Frances'
position in her fraternity has be effected by it—God knows if there
was anything I could do to make amends I would. Billy's very
upset over it and has said again and again, "You know, Mother, I
wouldn't deliberately do anything to harm Frances or any other
little girl." I personally feel both children acted on the impulse and
in the spirit of fun.

Truly, Billy has never been a problem in his life and all I
can say is that after a restricted life in New York City and military
school, the freedom of Texas has gone completely to his young
head—So please try to forgive and understand him if you can—

My one prayer is that he settle down and study for a
medical career that he himself has planned—John is not too well
and will need him very much in a few years—

We both sincerely apologize for all the unpleasantness that
has been yours to bear—

Love to all

Almeida Harris

Thursday

My Dear ———

I have returned from
New York and Billy has told
me of the unfortunate trip
to Galveston and the car
accident that occurred on
the way back to Austin —
Honestly it has taken several
days for me to recover from
the shock of it all — words
never seemed so empty, but
I want you and Nelson to
know how deeply grieved I
am that my boy could
ever have permitted Frances
to go on such a trip —

I'm grateful it was no
worse, but heart broken that
Frances' position in her
fraternity has been effected
by it — God knows if there
was anything I could do to
make amends I would —
Billy is very upset over it
and has said again and
again, "you know mother, I
wouldn't deliberately do anything
to harm Frances or any other
little girl." — I personally
feel both children acted
on the impulse — and
in the spirit of fun —

101

Truly Billy has never been
a problem in his life and
all I can say is that after
a restricted life in New York
City and military school,
the freedom of Texas has
gone completely to his young
head — So please try to
forgive and understand him
if you can —

My one prayer is that he
settle down and study for
a medical career that he
himself has planned — John
is not too well and will

need him very much in
a few years ———
    We both sincerely apologize
for all the unpleasantness
that has been yours to
bear ——— Love to all
            Almeida Harris

A letter from Bill's mother to Frances's mother shortly after the accident. The two women had been sorority sisters at the University and had known each other for many years.

University handled it. This is a sorority matter as well and we have to deal with it."

"Listen, if you have to take this out on anybody, take it out on me. Leave Frances alone. She's an innocent in all this."

"See you at 10 o'clock, Mr. Harris."

Bill slammed the receiver back into its cradle and called Frances.

"Sorry, Bill. She's not here," her roommate said.

"Where is she?"

"I can't say for certain, but I think she went to take her eight o'clock exam."

"Thanks." Bill hung up the phone, grabbed his books and headed for the exam.

As soon as he saw Frances he asked her if she received a phone call. With tears glistening in her eyes she nodded.

"Look, none of this is anyone's fault. Once they hear our side of the story, they've got to admit that we did the best we could under horrible circumstances. I can't imagine they'd do anything more than maybe place us under probation, and the dean's already done that."

"I hope you're right, Bill."

Just then the professor walked in and told everyone to take their seats. "Put all your books away and clear your desks of everything but a pen or pencil."

Bill and Frances looked at each other with trepidation as the professor placed stacks of the written test on the first desk of each row for the students to pass back.

Bill had to admit his mind wasn't on this test. All he could think of was what might happen at the upcoming meeting. Time crept by at an incredibly slow pace and for once he was grateful for it. It meant that the meeting would not come as quickly. He glanced over to Frances and saw her dab at her eyes once more with a hanky. She was very upset and he wished he could reach out and comfort her, but he knew better than to try that again. The last time had been bad enough.

"Pencils down!"

Bill looked at his watch and saw that it was 9:30. Frances glanced in his direction and forced a tiny smile. He smiled back. "It'll be all right. You'll see," he whispered. After they handed in their tests, together they walked to the Pi Phi House and waited outside the chapter room.

Several ladies had already arrived. Some were seated inside while others visited with each other in the hallway. Bill and Frances shrank against the wall hoping to avoid any unwanted attention.

The president emerged from the room and clapped her hands to get everyone's attention. Her eyes found Frances. Without any acknowledgement she looked back at the small crowd that had gathered. "Ladies. Shall we go inside to start the meeting?" She turned on her heels and the women followed suit, leaving Bill and Frances alone in the hall.

"What do you think they're doing in there?" she asked.

"Probably telling them what happened, or at least what they think happened. They'll probably call us in one at a time. Just tell them the way things happened. They'll have to understand."

Just then the door to the meeting room opened. "Frances Puett," the woman called.

When Frances looked at Bill, he read the anxiety, the nervousness, and most of all the fear. "Good luck."

She nodded and took a deep breath and followed the woman inside. The door closed with a thud and Bill leaned against the wall and slid to the floor. The minutes crept by with the speed of a snail, and it seemed as if every few seconds, Bill took another reading from his watch. More and more women arrived until sixty-five middle-aged alumni had passed through those doors, and not a single one even smiled as they passed by.

The situation, the June heat, and the closed hallway all conspired to make Bill feel as uncomfortable as he'd ever felt in his life. After what seemed like an eternity, although only thirty or forty minutes had passed, the door opened and Frances came out, sobbing.

Bill jumped to his feet but she ran right past him and out of the building.

"Frances!" He called after her but she never heard him, and never hesitated a moment in her hurry to flee.

"Bill Harris," the woman calmly called from the door.

Bill looked in the direction in which Frances had fled and then back at the waiting woman and then back to where Frances had gone.

"Mr. Harris, we're waiting for you," she said impatiently.

Bill turned and followed the woman into the room. She closed the door behind them and took her seat at the front.
He saw a group of stone-faced women sitting together in rows of folding chairs. One of the women gestured for him to sit behind a small table across from where they had gathered.

A goose necked lamp sat on the table, placed so that

when it was turned on, it shone directly into his eyes. That way he could hear but not see any of them. Bill had to close his eyes because the light was so bright.

After a few hostile questions it became clear that they were just trying to verify what Frances had told them and he did his best to make them understand that nothing improper had happened.

"We had all spent a pleasant day together at the beach and on the way home, the accident happened. People were severely injured. Mary Jo's car was a total wreck and crunched together like an accordion and we were unable to drive it. Besides, Mary Jo and Albert are our friends and we felt the best thing we could do was stay at the hospital, at least until we found out how serious their injuries were, and they were quite serious."

"But you spent the night in a hotel," one voice said.

"The sheriff himself arranged for separate rooms for us," Bill countered.

"You could have called someone at the University to come get you," another voice said.

"It was nearly midnight and I had no idea whom to call."

"But you didn't call anyone to tell them what happened as curfew neared."

Bill only sighed. This was impossible. It soon became clear to him that they were trying to verify what Frances had already told them. "We had been through a terrible accident. Our friends were seriously injured, maybe dying, and curfew was the last thing on our minds."

"That's obvious," someone said snidely.

"Look, no one was drinking. We did nothing wrong. We

left Galveston in plenty of time to arrive before curfew. We acted responsibly, but the accident happened and we were all victims. Under the circumstances we did the best we could and came back as soon as we could. We slept in separate rooms. You can call the hotel to verify. I don't understand what your problem is. You ought to be helping Frances, not conspiring to crucify her."

A murmur of discussion rose from the room.

"That will be all, Mr. Harris. You can go now."

Bill rose from his chair and raced from the room with Mrs. Bell's Boarding House as his destination.

"Please, Mrs. Bell. I've got to see Frances."

Mrs. Bell looked at him dubiously. "She's very upset, Bill. I don't know."

"Please. I've got to see her."

Mrs. Bell went to the phone and dialed Frances's number and handed the receiver to the young man.

"Frances, please come down. I need to talk to you."

Frances still sobbed. "No, Bill, I can't." She tried to catch her breath. "It was horrible. I can't see you right now," and she hung up the phone.

Hearing her voice on the phone made it clear to Bill just how upset Frances was. She was hysterical and didn't want to see him. Would she ever want to see him again? Slowly, he made his way back to his dorm and sat in his room, staring out the window the rest of the day.

After a sleepless night a call came down the hall. "Harris! Phone!"

Bill trudged down the hall to the phone. "Hello. This is Bill."

"Oh, Bill," she cried.

He recognized Frances's voice immediately. "What's wrong?"

"Those horrible women, those Pi Phi alums called my parents. On top of everything else they've done to me, they, they. . .," Frances was crying so hard he could hardly understand what she was saying. "Please help me, Bill. They say I've disgraced them and that I have to leave school. They say I have to go home now."

"Who said you have to leave school? Who says you've disgraced them?"

"My parents, Bill. My parents. The sorority expelled both Mary Jo and me. Poor Mary Jo is still in the hospital and they tell me she's going to be expelled too." She continued crying. "My father is loading up the car right now to take me home."

He didn't wait to hear more. He hung up the phone and ran to Mrs. Bell's faster than he'd ever run in his life. When he got there he saw Mr. and Mrs. Puett's car double parked in front of the dormitory. The trunk at the rear was open and he could see Frances lying in the back seat, crying her eyes out. Her mother, sitting in the front seat, was crying too.

Before he had a chance to say anything, her father came running downstairs carrying an armful of Frances's clothes. He ran right past Bill without a word and threw his armload of stuff into the trunk, then ran right back up the stairs for another load.

Already knowing what he would find, Bill walked to the back of the car and saw it loaded with Frances's clothes, books, and other possessions. Her father had evidently not even taken the time to fold her clothes into a suitcase. Rather, he had just thrown them every which way and they lay in wrinkled heaps among Frances's other things.

About the time the significance of what was happening really started sinking in, Mr. Puett arrived at the trunk with another armful of clothes. Bill tried to talk to him.

"Mr. Puett, sir," Bill said trying to get the man to look at him. "I'd like to talk to you." Bill offered his hand but Mr. Puett pushed it aside.

Frances's father looked directly at the young man, and Bill had never seen anyone's face look so dark and forbidding. Frances's father was a small man, about five-feet-eight-inches tall and less than a hundred fifty pounds, but he was so uncontrollably angry, that he frightened Bill.

He turned his face away and slammed the trunk closed. He turned, marched to the front of the car and sat behind the steering wheel and slammed the door.

"Mr. Puett, sir." Bill followed him but he never acknowledged his presence. He just had to talk to him and assure him that they had done nothing wrong.

At that moment Frances's father turned toward Bill. With a menacing tone in his lowered voice, the older man said through gritted teeth, "Young man, I hold you *totally responsible* for what has happened to my daughter. You may never see her again. You may never come to my home again and if I ever hear that you're anywhere in west Texas, I'll have you shot. Do you understand me?" With that, he slammed the car door, started the engine, and punched the accelerator, taking Frances home to Midland and out of Bill's life.

He stood aghast at the threat, at the anger. He stood bereft at the thought of a life without Frances. The engine roared as the car rolled away. The last thing he saw was the image of Frances, her cheeks stained with tears, her face betraying her sorrow as she looked at him through the rear window. She became smaller and smaller as the car sped away and then disappeared from view when it turned the corner.

He didn't know how long he stood there, crying in the shadow of the boarding house, beneath the huge oak tree, with tears streaming down his face. He felt angry. He felt helpless. He felt that awful, hollow feeling inside his chest that comes with profound loss.

"Bill." A soft tentative voice broke through the despair and when he looked, he saw a friendly face.

"Carolyn," he croaked.

"Yes, come on over to the swing. Let's talk," she said softly.

Bill nodded and let her take his arm. She led him to the swing that Mrs. Bell had in her front yard. Together, they sat on the swing with Carolyn's arm draped over Bill's shoulder.

"Now you have to get a hold of yourself, Bill," she said.

"But Frances is gone. I'll never see her again."

"Do you really believe that, Bill Harris?"

He had learned early in life that whenever anyone used his first and last name, they were getting testy. But what the hell, he felt just as testy. "Yes, Carolyn Hopkins, I really believe that, and her father has the firepower to make sure of it."

When she gave him a questioning look, he told her about the threat Frances's father had made.

"Oh, my God, he didn't?"

111

"He did."

"Oh," Carolyn said and gave the swing another push. "What happened at the Pi Phi house?"

Through his tears he told Carolyn about what had happened. "Those old biddies called us into the room separately. I don't know what happened when Frances was in there but she came out running and crying. I've never seen her so upset. Then when I got in there, they asked me all kinds of rude questions." He paused to look at Carolyn. "We didn't do anything wrong!"

"I know. I know." She tried to soothe him. "That's exactly what Frances said. Sometimes I wish they would mind their own business."

"Mary Jo and Albert could have died! And all they were concerned about was that we missed our curfew. How sick is that? And now her parents have pulled her out of school and forbidden me to see her ever again. I can't stay here, Carolyn."

"Now, Bill. You have to stay here. You have to finish school and get your degree."

He looked toward the campus. "I can't stay here anymore. This place makes me sick." He stood up and took a few steps then turned back to Carolyn. "Will you give me a lift out to the highway?"

"Oh, Bill. Don't do anything foolish. Just give things a few days to settle down before you make any kind of decision."

He shook his head. "There can be no other decision for me. Frances is gone. I have to leave. I don't think I can walk around this place without expecting to see her come toward me with that smile."

"But, Bill, you have a scholarship."

"It doesn't matter. I can walk away from that. I just can't walk away from Frances like this."

"Maybe she'll be back in the fall," Carolyn suggested.

Bill shook his head. "You didn't see the look on her father's face. He's not going to let her out of his sight ever again."

She tried to reason with him, but it was no use. His mind was made up. He had never felt so terrible in his whole life. He wanted to die and he crumpled to the ground and let the tears flow until he had no more tears left. People passed by and asked Carolyn what was wrong.

"A broken heart," was her answer and they went on their way.

Bill was barely aware of what went on around him. Finally, he convinced Carolyn to give him a ride to the highway and he hitched a ride home to Houston. The semester had been a total loss, he forfeited his scholarship and he had lost the only girl he had ever loved, the love of his life. He wanted to die.

Bill stuck out his thumb and the first car that came by stopped and picked him up. As they rode east on 71 toward LaGrange and Houston, they passed right by the scene of the wreck.

The driver stopped so Bill could take a closer look. He walked over to the two cars, still waiting to be towed away. He opened the door to the small Chevy and looked inside for anything that might have been left behind, but found nothing. He scraped up some pieces of broken glass and put it in his shirt pocket and cried the rest of the way home to his mother's house on Banks Street in Houston.

Frances (right foreground in the dark dress) and Pi Phi girls at a water fight with the boys next door. All the girls, including Frances were soaked to the skin.

Frances playing Santa Claus at a DKE House party, in December, 1949.

Beta Homecoming Party October 22, 1949. Frances is in the center of the group (wearing the white blouse). Just before she met Bill.

Pi Phi open house for DKE, May, 1950. Bill and Frances pictured in foreground.

Note Bill sent to Frances asking her to map out where to meet.

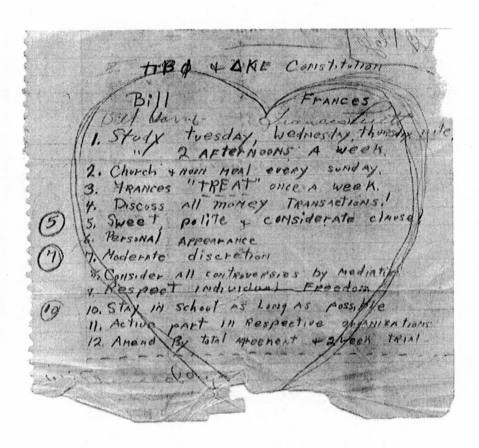

The "Constitution" signed by Bill and Frances early in the spring of 1950. Witnessed by Angela and Johnny Crawford. It laid out a code of behavior for the young couple to follow.

Frances and Bill at a party in 1950.

Bill Milburn, a friend, and Frances at a DKE party with friends.

Frances (middle) in the bathing suit competition
in a Texas beauty pageant.

p

PI BETA PHI

June 1950
Good Grief
Beautiful letter
Sunday night.

Dear Frances.

I'm sorry that I didn't get to see you before you left. I was going to come over tonite, because I was sick today.

I'm awfully disappointed that you didn't stay to take your exams. You spent a whole semester sweating it out for nothing.

Of course, the main reason for this letter is to tell you "chin up, and stick to your guns." You're taking an awful lot, and I know how humiliated and hurt you must be. It probably seems very unfair to you and it does to me, too. In fact, I think, that it's us who will suffer, too. It's not right for a bunch of people to set themselves up to judge another human being. You did wrong in lying, admitted, but which of us can say that we've been so clear and pure to say that you should be punished for that! I'm sorry it happen-

122

...et and believe me, I didn't want it too. And not only me, but the whole chapter was against it. The only reason your pin was taken by us is that some, or most, believed that if we didn't national would take it permanently and nobody wanted that to happen to you.

Frances, I and others, really want you to come back. I'll tell you the reason why. People aren't going to believe our reasons for taking the pin. They're going to think things were much worse than they were. I want you to come back and get that pin back if you have anything to do with the Phi again as long as you live, in which case I wouldn't blame you. But just to show people that you weren't, to put it crudely, just kicked out.

I'll say this in the chapter's defense. They honestly believe that national would pick the pin permanently and since they all want you, they are taking the lesser of the two evils.

But do come back and do good...

and I think you'll never be sorry. It's an awful experience, I know, but put it on your list of bad luck and try not to think about it too much.

Let me hear from you and if you're ever coming my way, let me know and "I'll bake a cake and spread the welcome mat for you."

Love,
Pat.

Another letter of encouragement to Frances after she left school and was expelled from the sorority.

Aug. 26, 1950

Dear Frances,

I have just returned from a trip up East to Baltimore. It was wonderful getting away from hot ole Houston and enjoyed the cool spell we had while in Baltimore. I have been hoping to hear a word from you telling me you were going to be in Houston. Remember you said you'd need someone to pal around with in the day time and when & if you came down and I've been ready & waiting but no Frances! Anytime you will be coming please let me know.

Upon my return I also learned of your not returning to school and also of your misfortune.

125

Frances, I hope I don't need to tell you how we all feel about it down here — especially me.

It was in the full sense of the word a "misfortune" and could we have prevented the consequence believe me — we would have. You know I would have. It could have happened to me or to anyone of us. I didn't know exactly what to say in this letter but I did want you to know we're all with you and what has happened hasn't made you any less of a sister to me or any of the rest. Please believe this.

I'm tempted myself not to return to school at the moment — with the world in the condition it's in. There won't be any help in the school for one thing. They are going to being drafted in

flocks & droves. This boy that
I have been going with has
been drafted and will be off
in September. It's just awful!
Someone was telling me the
other day that during the last
war there were four boys in
the Phi Gam house and three
left in the Phi Delt house. That
just shows you the state things
will probably be in soon again.
And everyone getting married too.
I've never seen anything like
the way people are marrying.
It's almost a fad.

Have seen Bill once in
awhile and he seems to be
working hard. Guess you know
how hard he works!

Well, all for now. Please
drop me a line if you have time.
Love,
Pilla

Sunday

Dearest Frances,

How can I ever tell you how very much I appreciated and enjoyed the party that you and Dorothy gave for me? Everything was wonderful! The refreshments were delicious, the company was delightful, and the present you gave me was lovely. Really, those earrings are the cutest I ever saw. A thousand thanks for everything!

Frances, I still am at a loss for words to tell you how sorry I am about what happened at school. Certainly you are to be commended for the brave way in which you are facing it and the frank, calm way in which you are able to dis-

cult it. I know from the spirit
you show that you will be able
to work things out.
Do visit Austin and Houston
often this fall. Thanks again for
the delightful party and gift.
Love,
Louise

In spite of Frances's expulsion from the sorority, she received a lot of support from her many friends. These letters are just a few examples.

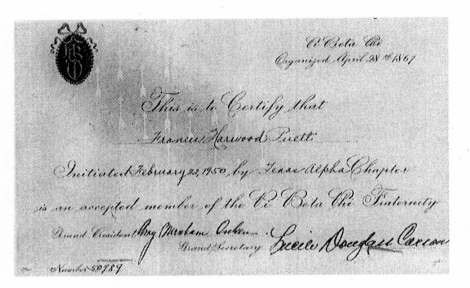

Frances's certification of initiation into the
Pi Beta Phi Sorority on February 20, 1950.

Frances's dismissal from the sorority on July 15, 1950

Dear Frances,

I was certainly sorry to hear about the wreck and it's consequences and I surely hope that everything works out allright! I feel sure that time will help your problems alot.

Midland was really full of people this last week! The rodeo & golf tournament both being at the same time made this quite the town for out of town visitors. I saw Roane the other day and he has grown so much — I really couldn't get over how he has grown up.

Abbie had about 7 girls out visiting her so I've been with them alot, however they're all gone home now and we really do miss them - it was so much fun having them here!

Be sure & write me up at Santa Rosa - I'll be up there for about 10 days - I'm leaving Monday. Tell me all about camp & what you do.

Frances, let me say again how sorry I am, but how glad I am that your probation & all is only temporary! I mentioned it to no one but when questioned I've explained that the situation is _temporary_.

I saw your mother at a party yesterday morning & got to chat with her a minute. I want to go by & see her if I have a chance before going to the country! (over)

132

our house up there should
be finished when we get
up there & so Muddy & I
have really been busy packing.
Tell Pat hello for me &
try not to worry lots & please
know I'm thinking of you.
                    As Ever,
                        Mumzy

P.S.
My address is just Santa Rosa,
New Mexico. Box 297

A letter to Frances from her friend Mumzy after the automobile
accident and leaving school.

Frances cutting the cake with new husband, Charles Black. They were married in January, 1951. Their son Charles was born in September of 1951.

Bill and Mary, his first wife. They were married only a few months. They divorced shortly after the birth of her son.

Chapter 12

"Bill! What a surprise! I didn't expect to see you home until next week." His mother followed him into the house and up the stairs to his room.

At his bedroom door he turned, hugged his mother, then retreated into his closed, dark room.

His mother knocked at the door. "Bill, what's wrong? What happened? Where are your things?"

"Please, Mother, I just need some time alone."

"But, Bill."

"Please, Mother," he pleaded.

He knew she was still standing outside his door because he had not heard her footsteps retreating down the hall. For two days he remained closeted in his room. If it weren't so hot, he'd have drawn his curtain, but he needed the air to breathe, no easy feat in Houston in June, but then he thought suffocation might be a neat way to end it all. Morning, noon, and night, his mother came to his room with meals and snacks, questioning after his health, and always a request. "Please, Bill, tell me what happened."

"I can't. Not now," was always his reply.

Even his father, still somewhat debilitated from his stroke, tried to get an explanation from Bill. He tried to get

136

him to come out of his room, but to no avail. Finally, after two days and worried beyond anything she had known before started calling her friends in Austin to see if they knew anything about what had happened. Eventually, she found someone who told her.

"Well, Frances Puett, you know Frances, in fact her mother is a Pi Phi, but you knew that, anyway, she went to Galveston one day with Bill and a couple of friends, and on the way back they were in a car accident and then. . .hospital. . .sheriff. . .hotel. . .curfew. . .sorority. . .probation. . . .

"Well, Frances's reputation was completely ruined and of course at this point no one knows what kind of future that poor girl will have and it's the biggest thing that's happened to the Pi Phi's in fifty years. So they kicked her out as an example. After all, the chapter has to maintain its standards, you know the ideal standard set by the national leadership and all that. . . reputation. . .back to Midland. . . .Bill forfeited his scholarship, didn't take any exams, and it's all your son's fault."

Bill's mother hung up the phone and marched up the stairs to Bill's room. She banged on the door. "Bill Harris, you open this door and let me in right now!"

She waited a moment and just about the time she was going to knock again, Bill opened the door.

He stood before her with his dirty clothes, rumpled hair, and tear stained face. "Oh, Mother, you just wouldn't believe. . . ."

"Shh, I heard. Now tell me your side of the story." She went into the room and closed the door behind her and listened to what Bill had to tell her.

137

"Well, if what you say is true, and I have no reason to doubt you, neither one of you did anything wrong, and everybody overreacted. What about Mary Jo and Albert? Will they be okay?"

Bill nodded. "They're still in the hospital and will be for another week or two, but the doctors say they'll recover."

"Well, then. This is all a big to do about nothing. Let's see what we can do to get your scholarship back and get you back in school."

"But I don't want to go back," Bill protested.

"Of course you do. Now, let's see." His mother rose from the bed and left the room mumbling to herself.

Bill knew that when she did that, she was making plans and he was sure that every one of them had something to do with getting him back to school.

A week or two later, Bill received a post card informing him of the dates of make-up exams. It urged him to come back and take them so he could receive final grades for his classes. It didn't matter that he had no desire to do so, his parents insisted that he go back to Austin, not only to take his exams but find a way to stay in school.

Bill finally relented and went back to UT on the appointed day to take his make-up exams. He arrived a few minutes before the eight o'clock bell sounded and looked around for an empty chair. As he perused the room the sight of Frances stunned him. Sitting way off in a corner all by herself, she looked terribly sad.

He rushed over to her, terrified that she would bolt and run as soon as she saw him. Like Hester in *The Scarlet Letter* he felt as if he had a huge sign on his chest that read "Doctor

Death, the harbinger of bad tidings, failure and pain."

Instead, when she looked up and saw him, she smiled her most wonderful Frances smile and Bill immediately decided he wasn't going to kill himself after all. Her smile had saved his miserable life.

"All right, everyone," the monitor said. "Take your seats."

Frantically, Bill said. "We need to talk afterward."

Frances nodded.

After the exam, Bill and Frances went to a small coffee shop. He learned that Frances had received the same post card he had. "And since my father didn't know we had taken all the same courses this semester, he allowed me to come back. He said I had to finish what I started."

"Does that mean you get to come back in the fall?" he asked full of hope.

Frances shook her head. "No, Bill. I'm sorry. I can't come back. What about you?"

"My parents want me to come back, but I don't want to. It won't be the same without you here. Besides, I've forfeited my scholarship."

"Bill! You didn't!"

"I did."

"Well, you'll just have to get it back. You need your degree. You've got to go out in the world and make a living."

"And what about you, Frances? Don't you need your degree?"

"No, I'm a woman. I'll probably marry somebody and take care of the house and the kids," she said sadly.

The thought of Frances as somebody else's wife, the

139

mother of someone else's children, made his heart feel as though an iron band were squeezing the life out of it. He had to change the subject.

"So where are you staying. I mean, all the dorms and boarding houses are closed for the summer."

"I'm staying at my uncle's house. He and my aunt live in a town called Fentress, down by San Marcos. Where are you?"

"No place yet. I only drove up here early this morning. I guess I'll find a motel to stay in for a few days."

They talked a little while longer, carefully avoiding anything about the accident or what had happened with the Pi Phi's or her father.

Finally, Bill said, "I guess I'd better get started looking for a place to stay."

Frances placed her hand on his arm. "Listen, Bill," she said with another heart stopping smile. "My aunt's house is huge, tons of rooms, bedrooms, I mean. There's just no reason for you to spend money staying in some motel somewhere when you can spend a few days there."

Her words had made him so happy, but he had a few misgivings. "Don't they know how your father feels about me?"

"I don't think so. It's not something he's proud of. I don't see any reason why he would even tell my uncle, but I can find out easily enough. Please, Bill, come to San Marcos with me."

He smiled and nodded. "Sounds like a good idea."

She leaned over and brushed her lips against his cheek, then stood and reached for his hand as though to pull him out of his chair. "Let's go down there and see what they say."

He followed Frances to Fentress in his car and waited behind a bunch of shrubs that shielded her aunt's house from the street. He waited while Frances went inside to find out if they'd heard anything about their tragedy. As it turned out Frances was right. Her father hadn't said a word to his brother-in-law about it and they welcomed Frances's friend with open arms.

The house, a large one by any standards, had three stories with at least seven bedrooms and Frances's aunt and uncle were delighted that someone would put one to good use.

Frances and Bill were the very ideal of propriety during the three days they took their make-up exams and Bill managed to get his scholarship back and reinstated in school as his parents had told him to do. But they talked to each other about everything. They discussed and argued and promised and agreed until, at last, they put their lives together again. Those three days were so happy for Bill, he wished they never had to come to an end, but as good things always do, they did.

When their exams were over, Frances drove back home to Midland and Bill had to go to Virginia for a six-week ROTC summer camp. While Bill was in Virginia, he wrote to her, passionate letters, every night, and mailed every one of them the first thing the next morning. But Frances never wrote back, not a single letter.

He couldn't understand why she didn't write. They had meant so much to each other and they had been through so much together. Why didn't she write?

He went through life numb, feeling bereft of the love and

joy he had found in his life with Frances. The summer passed and Bill continued to write. Every day he waited anxiously for the mailman to drop the envelopes into the mail slot of his front door. He'd rifle through them hoping for something from Frances, but nothing came.

He'd heard from friends that Frances's father decided that she would not be going back to UT in the fall. He had been right about that. He had also heard that her father had made her get a job with Shell Oil Company. Her father had forced her to get on with her life. What would he do without his Frances? He had no idea.

Chapter 13

"Harris! Haven't you learned how to run that play yet?" Coach Jungmichael shouted across the field. "The game is this weekend. You're the key to this whole play!"

Bill had been received back into UT and retrieved his football scholarship. Though still only August, and classes would not start for another few days, Bill had to report early for a two-week football camp. He had done what was expected of him but his heart wasn't in it.

This fall of 1950 would not be what Bill had envisioned it could be. In the spring, he had looked forward to at least two more years with Frances, attending classes, dances, concerts and parties with her. He had looked forward to her waiting for him outside the locker room after football games so they could spend some time together.

Instead, he was alone. As he passed by this bench or that tree, a memory from only months ago would reach out and take hold of his heart. He pictured her leaning against the tree and laughing while he teased her about something silly. He remembered how they sat on that bench and studied together.

When his classes started, thoughts of her smile filled his mind instead of history or philosophy. Sometimes, he half expected to look over to the seat beside him to see her sitting there, but always felt a keen disappointment when all he saw was one of his football buddies.

He attended classes. He went to practice. He did his homework and studied, but he found no joy. To pass time, he wrote letters to Frances. More and more he thought of mailing them as an exercise in futility. She had not answered any of his missives and she was not likely to now.

Then one day, one of Frances's friends came up to him on campus.

"Hello, Bill," she said.

Bill nodded. He couldn't remember her name but her face looked familiar.

"I thought you might want to know that Frances will be at the OU game in Dallas!"

"Really?" He couldn't believe his good fortune.

She nodded.

"Thank you! Thank you!" Suddenly, all thought of the game escaped his mind. Instead, he thought only of seeing Frances again. "Please tell her I'd love to see her again. Tell her to come to the stadium, knock on the dressing room door and I'll come out and talk to her."

Bill thought the next two weeks would never pass. He literally crossed off each day on his calendar as it ended, and grew happier with each completed day because that brought him closer to his Frances.

The day finally arrived, and while Bill was in the dressing room at Cotton Bowl Stadium locker room with his teammates, someone came to the door.

"Harris, somebody here to see you."

Bill nearly catapulted through the door with anticipation.

He ran down the long, narrow hallway toward the exit, just wanting to see her smile, just wanting to laugh with her, just wanting to hold her once more. He opened the door and there she stood.

"Hello, Bill," she said shyly, almost as if they were strangers.

"Frances." He uttered her name almost as if it were a prayer.

In less than a heartbeat they were in each other's arms, holding on for dear life, holding on as if they never wanted to let go.

"This is such a wonderful surprise! I'm so happy you came to the game. How long will you stay? My, how can you stay? There are no hotel rooms left in Dallas because of the big game."

Frances looked at the ground and then back up at Bill. "I have to catch a plane tonight, right after the game. We won't really have any time together, but I had to see you. Are you all right?"

Bill took her hands in both of his. "How can I be all right without you?" He looked up to see tears shimmering in her eyes. "Frances, don't cry. Don't go back tonight. Stay an extra day."

"I can't, Bill. Besides, I don't have anywhere to stay."

"We'll get you a room."

"What? How? Like you said, there are no rooms left in Dallas."

Bill didn't bother going back into the dressing room or telling anyone where he was going. Instead, he took her by the hand and led her to her rental car. He opened the door for her and when she was seated, settled himself into the passenger's seat.

"Where are we going?" she asked.

"Someplace where we can talk and be alone. Where are your things?"

She pointed to the single overnight bag in the back seat.

"But what about the game? The team expects you in there," she protested.

"I'll get back in time to dress for the game, so let's spend this time together."

Frances drove out of the parking lot and together they spent the next few hours looking for a hotel room, but because of the game, there was not a vacancy to be had in either Fort Worth or Dallas.

"Do you think the fates are trying to tell us something?" Frances asked.

"Sure do. We just can't give up."

Bill directed here to head west. Finally, several miles west of Fort Worth, they came to a Motel 3, a little place that looked like it had seen better days, many years in the past.

"I don't know about this place, Bill. It looks pretty seedy."

"Frances, we're desperate for a room. Come on."

They parked in front of the office and went inside to register. Frances followed.

"I'd like a room for the night, please."

The cigar smoking clerk looked up from his desk to see a young couple standing on the other side of it. "You two from the college?" he asked warily.

"What? The college here in town?" Bill asked.

146

The clerk nodded.

"No, sir. We're Mr. and Mrs. Thompson from out of town and we'd like a room."

The clerk chomped down on his cigar and eyed them another moment. "Sure you are." Then he pushed the registration book toward them with a pen. Bill signed it. "That'll be $3," the clerk said.

Bill took out his wallet and slid three ones across the counter and the clerk handed him the key to a room.

"Thank you, sir." Bill reached for Frances's hand and led the way to number 12.

For the next 18 hours, Bill and Frances lay in each others' arms, talking, kissing, crying, holding on to the past and hoping they had a future together.

When he asked her about his letters, Frances gave him a puzzled look. "What letters?"

"I'll bet your mother or father intercepted them. That's why you never got them. I wrote you so many letters, sometimes two a day, always expecting to hear from you. But when I didn't, I thought you had forgotten about me."

"Bill, I could never forget about you."

And they talked, and loved, and kissed and talked.

Finally, early on Sunday morning, Frances said, "Bill, I really have to get home. My father will probably be very upset as it is. He expected me last night."

Bill nodded. "I know. I just hope you won't be in too much trouble with him."

She smiled. "Whatever trouble I get into with my father, will be worth it. I got to spend this time with you," and she melted into his arms once more.

Bill waited with Frances at the airport until her flight was called and he gave her a long, hard kiss. "That's got to last me until we meet again."

"I hope it'll be soon," she said just before she walked down the breezeway and into the plane.

As Frances's plane left the gate on its way back to Midland, Frances began to cry. Bill saw her through the window and wondered what had happened. She had been so happy.

Years later, Bill learned that she had had an engagement ring sitting in her purse. Charles Black lived in Midland and he had proposed. She had come to Dallas to give Bill one last chance to ask her to marry him. He had told her hundreds of times how much he loved her, but when he had not asked her that all important question, she put Chuck's ring on her finger and started planning her wedding.

As much as he wanted to, Bill hadn't proposed because with no money, no help from home, and with eight years of medical training ahead of him, he knew he could never support them.

They were so young, so inexperienced, and they had failed at their last opportunity to be together.

Chapter 14

Over the next few weeks, hope rose in Bill's heart. Maybe if enough time passed, her father would calm down and allow him to see her. Maybe if he went to the man, hat in hand, they could talk it out. Bill was a proud young man, and he wouldn't do that for just anyone, but Frances was not just anyone.

Then in November, Bill received his first letter from Frances. When he opened the envelope, his DKE pin fell to the floor. He bent and picked it up, then he looked in the envelope and found a newspaper clipping. When he unfolded the enclosed paper, he saw his beautiful Frances smiling back at him. She was as perfect as he had remembered her. His Frances. Then he read the words beneath the photo, *Announce Engagement – Mr. and Mrs. Nelson Puett announce the engagement and approaching marriage of their daughter, Frances, to Charles A. Black, Jr. son of Mr. and Mrs. Alfred Black of Wichita, Kansas. . . .*

The paper slipped to the floor and Bill felt his knees give out. He sank onto his bed and with his head resting in his hands cried like a baby.

"Harris!" The pounding on the door and someone calling his name brought him out of his dark place. He recognized

ANNOUNCE ENGAGEMENT – Mr. and Mrs. Nelson Puett announce the engagement and approaching marriage of their daughter, Frances, to Charles A. Black, Jr., son of Mr. and Mrs. Charles A. Black of Wichita, Kan. The announcement was made to friends at an open house Friday night in the home of the bride-elect's parents. Miss Puett attended Gulf Park College in Gulfport, Mississippi and the University of Texas. The couple will be married January 27 in the First Presbyterian Church.

the voice as one of the linebackers on the football team. He dare not let anyone see him in this state.

He took a deep breath. "Yes?"

"Time for practice," the voice said.

"Sorry. I'm not going. I'm sick," Bill shouted through the door. It wasn't a lie. He was sick at heart.

"All right. I'll tell the coach."

Bill heard the retreating footsteps and looked down at his feet to where the newspaper clipping had fluttered. He read the rest of the notice. She was getting married in January. She would be someone else's wife and have someone else's children. She was gone from his life forever. Convinced he would never find love or happiness with anyone else, Bill lay on his bed. Facing the wall, he cried himself to sleep.

Somehow, Bill got through the holidays with family and friends and went back to school in January. The date, January 27, 1951 loomed large and hurtful in his heart and he dreaded its arrival.

"Look, Bill, I know this is tough on you, but she's marrying someone else," his roommate said.

"I've got to do something. She's getting married next week."

"What can you do? Stop the wedding?"

Bill rose from his desk chair and shouted. "That's it!"

"What?"

"Stop the wedding."

"You're kidding, right?"

"Not at all. I'll just drive out there to Midland and when the minister gets to that part in the ceremony, you know, 'If anyone here can give just cause,' I'll stand up and give just cause."

"And what might that be?"

"I love her and she loves me."

"I'm sure her father will love that," his roommate reminded him.

"Then I will have died trying to win her back."

Early on the morning of January 27, Bill got in his roommate's car and began the long trek out to Midland. It took hours, but he had to get there before the wedding at seven in the evening. He stopped along the way only for food and fuel and hit the road again.

All the while he wondered how she felt about this marriage. Was she excited? Was she happy? Was she in love with him? Did she look forward to a future with this man? Or was she as miserable without him as he was without her? He didn't wish unhappiness for her, but he found it difficult to hope that she'd be happy with this Charles Black, whoever he was.

He arrived at the Church, late, the wedding had begun. Then he heard it, the organ playing, "Here Comes the Bride." He felt his whole body tremble as adrenaline flooded his system. This was fight or flight and certainly, if he wanted Frances, he'd have to fight for her.

He ran into the church and leaned against the back wall. The ceremony had begun but he watched with hopeful heart. Perhaps he could stop this wedding.

He listened as the minister gave the usual introduction about the solemnity of marriage and that this was not something you went into lightly. He knew he faced two huge problems. The first was to stop the service, and the second was Frances's father.

Bill had no idea if he'd be alive 15 minutes from now. Given the circumstances, he didn't think his chances were particularly good. Eventually, the minister got around to the ceremony itself, and he finally came to the part that Bill was waiting for.

"If anyone here can show just cause why Charles and Frances should not marry. . . ."

Bill waved his arms vigorously and strode up the aisle. A murmured whisper rose from the crowd as he passed each pew. While neither Frances nor Charles were aware of his presence, the minister was.

Immediately recognizing what was about to happen, he rushed through the vows and ended with, "I now pronounce you man and wife."

Bill stopped dead in his tracks. He wanted to shout, to scream to yell. No! This had not happened. He came all the way from Austin to stop it and the minister had foiled him.

He turned on his heel, burst into sobs and without another look, without a word, numbly drove back to Austin. His tears blurred the road ahead of him and his heart broke as he came to the realization that he'd never love again.

Chapter 15

Staying in school took all his courage. Everywhere he went, he saw something that reminded him of Frances. Every song he heard, brought a memory of her to mind. Every time he drank a Coke, or walked to class, he wished she were still with him. While walking around campus, sometimes, he'd find himself on the path to Mrs. Bell's or to some other familiar haunt that he had shared with her.

In short, he was miserable and alone. He couldn't understand how things had gone so wrong. Then he looked in the trunk of his car, and there were the things he and Frances had bought from the basement of Scarborough's for their first apartment. He couldn't bear the sight of those unopened packages and slammed the lid shut. The small coffee pot, the frying pan, even the plastic dishes, all reminded him too much of the unfulfilled hopes he had shared with Frances.

Bill's friends told him over and over he had to deal with it, get over it, and go on with his life. At first, he thought them unfeeling and uncaring. Couldn't they understand how deeply his hurt ran? Apparently not. But with the passage of time, he grew more depressed. He learned to drink beer and used it to numb the pain.

He'd graduate in a couple of years and everyone would

expect him to go out into the world to make his living. But at what? He had changed his major from pre-med to education so that he could take the same classes as Frances, but he didn't really want to be a teacher. Now without Frances here, he changed his major back to pre-med, but his heart wasn't in it and his grades fell to D's and F's with a few B's and C's.

He trudged through the spring semester, the summer and most of the fall, always looking for Frances just around the corner, but never found her.

"That's the way to go, Harris!" Coach Jungmichael praised him for something he had done on the field and his teammates slapped him on the back in recognition of the rare accomplishment.

"All right, ladies! Showers!" Coach commanded. He took up his clipboard and headed for the locker room.

The shower room in the stadium was big enough for about seventy football players to shower together. That meant that fifty or more boys would dress for supper and cross San Jacinto Street at the same time.

For a whole week, Bill hadn't noticed the pretty blonde girl sitting in the Chevy convertible, and he walked right past her. Finally, one day he crossed San Jacinto all alone and the girl spoke to him.

"Hi, Bill Harris. I'm mad at you!"

Her unusual greeting took him by surprise and made him stop in his tracks.

"You've walked by me every day for a week and never even spoke to me."

"Excuse me, do I know you?"

"You certainly do. You danced with me at the Short Horn

155

Bar about two weeks ago. I had a date with Bud Nott from Abilene."

"Mary?"

"Yes, Mary." She crossed her arms over her chest and nodded, pretending to be upset with him.

"Oh, Mary, I was drinking beer that night and I don't really remember you."

"Well, get in the car and I'll give you a lift up the hill to Hill Hall."

Bill started to decline her invitation but decided to take her up on her offer and got into the passenger seat. Mary drove right past Hill Hall and kept on going toward south Austin to a drive-in called The Shrimp Boat on South First Street.

Mary ordered two shrimp platters and paid for both. While they ate their meals in the car, facing each other, Bill realized that Mary was flirting with him. With her seat as far back from the steering wheel as it would go, she crossed and uncrossed her legs; moved her shoulders sensuously; and when she laughed, threw her head all the way back.

He became uncomfortable and turned toward the window. As soon as they finished their shrimp, Mary drove Bill back to the campus and drove into the parking lot near his dorm. Without lights and without benefit of the moon, the lot was pitch black. She pulled up under a live oak tree and parked. He could feel her staring at him through the blackness, but didn't say a word.

Finally, Mary broke the silence. "Bill, are you hot?" she asked as she slid closer to him.

He cleared his throat. "As a matter of fact, Mary, I'm

very comfortable."

She slid still closer. "Well, I'm burning up." She pulled her blouse up over her head and sat inches from him with her body, nude from the waist up.

Her action surprised him and he blinked, looked away, then looked back.

Mary giggled and raised her hands over her head. "Bill, do you like my breasts?"

Bill knew the only answer to that question. "Mary, you have lovely breasts."

She slid still closer to him and she insinuated herself into his arms. A few minutes later, Mary taught Bill the facts of life and for the first time in his life, Bill entered into an intimate relationship with someone, a girl he hardly knew.

Chapter 16

Mary waited for Bill after practice every day, and afterward they'd go behind the baseball stadium for more "lessons" until school broke for the Christmas holidays. Bill went home to Houston and Mary went to Abilene. Over the holidays she resumed a relationship with her high school boyfriend and became pregnant.

After the holidays, everyone went back to the University to take their finals and Bill saw Mary.

"How were your holidays?" he asked making conversation.

"Fine," she said shyly.

He looked at her curiously. He had never known her to be shy about anything. "What's wrong?"

"Bill, we need to talk."

"Fine. Let's go for a walk."

Together they strolled through the campus in silence.

"I thought you wanted to talk," he said.

"I did. I do." She stopped and Bill followed suit. She lowered her voice to barely above a whisper. "Bill, I missed my period."

A jolt of realization shot through him, but he didn't want to think about reality. "So what does that mean?" He knew it was a stupid question, but he had nothing else to say. He had always heard about stupid questions that men ask in times like these, now he could add his name to the list.

"Bill, it means I'm pregnant," she said adamantly.

"When are you due?"

"I suppose sometime in the fall."

The words shocked and horrified him. True they'd been having sex for months, but he never considered the possibility of a baby. Besides, he was never in love with Mary.

For the next three weeks, Bill thought about what to do without ever talking it over with anyone. Abortion was completely out of the question. Not only was it illegal, but the idea was repugnant to him. He couldn't bear the thought of killing his own child before it had the chance to draw its first breath. Desertion, another alternative, was not an option. It simply wasn't the honorable thing to do. The only honorable course of action was to marry her.

On January 26, 1952, Bill and Mary secretly married at a Justice of the Peace. Bill's good friends Cliff and Taffy Goldsmith were the only witnesses. All the while, the thought that something was wrong kept coming to mind, such as, how could he be sure that this child was even his? Soon, just as Mary had predicted, she started to "show," and after spring break when Mary went home to Abilene, she failed to return to school.

When Mary did not return to school, Bill had himself tested and armed with letters from two medical doctors, both urologists, he confronted Mary's father. They sat in Mr. White's car, a brand new black Cadillac, a place where they could talk quietly.

"So, you're the father of Mary's baby," the older man said when meeting Bill for the first time.

"No, sir. I'm only married to her."

Mr. White eyed Bill suspiciously. "What are you saying?"

"I'm saying I married Mary thinking I was the father of her baby, but that title has to go to somebody else." Bill presented the letters to Mr. White. "As you can see, each of these letters contains a lab report stating I'm sterile, therefore, I couldn't possibly be the father of Mary's child."

Mr. White's face went red. He reached into his glove compartment, and when he opened it, Bill saw a gun. Bill didn't want to be looking down the barrel of that gun and he stayed Mr. White's hand. He also knew that Mary's father was angry enough to pull the trigger given the chance. He had to get the gun away from him.

For the next minute, one of the longest minutes of his life, Bill and Mary's father struggled over the pistol in the confines of that Cadillac. Neither gave an inch and finally, the younger, more powerful man prevailed and Mr. White put the gun away.

"We've got to come to some kind of agreement," Bill said gathering his wits about him.

Mr. White nodded and they found a solution to the problem. Bill stayed married to Mary for six more months until after the baby was born in September. Afterward, Mary filed for divorce, which he willingly agreed to. He also agreed to never see her or her baby again, Michael G. Harris. Eventually, Mary remarried and her new husband adopted her little boy.

After the episode with Frances's father and this one with Mary's father, Bill's self-esteem cratered. He gave up on the idea of ever marrying again and didn't even bother looking at other women, and forgot about dating, until about a year later when he met a girl, Bette, in one of his classes.

One day after class she asked him out for a coffee. On their third date, he told her about Frances and Mary and she demanded that he take her home. Bill thought it was over. Then several months later, Bette saw him on campus and pulled her car up beside him.

"Bill, let me give you a lift to wherever you're going."

This was the second time in his life that a girl had done this and a little warning flag went up in his head, but he got in the car anyway. "I didn't think you were ever going to talk to me again."

"Well, I have to admit I was a little leery of you, but I asked some of my friends about you?"

"And? What did they say?"

"Let's just say I got some good reports about you. Will you forgive me?"

Bill smiled and nodded. "I suppose I can do that."

Chapter 17

In 1953, Bette and Bill began seeing each other again. Bill graduated from UT with a degree in biology. He had not totally given up on his idea to attend medical school and applied but was turned down.

On June 3, 1954, Bill received his military orders to report for duty. He reported as ordered to Fort Belvoir in Virginia and was inducted into the army as a 2nd Lieutenant. In September, he reapplied to medical school and was once again refused entrance.

In the meantime, Bette pursued him by phone and letter and on September 26, 1954, Bill married Bette in a big church wedding in Austin, Texas. On the fourth day of their honeymoon in New Orleans, Bill's cousin, Dr. Hunter Harris, and his wife Catherine invited the newlyweds for dinner.

During the course of the evening, Dr. Harris turned to Bill and asked, "Bill, whatever became of Frances?"

Bette blanched at the mention of Frances's name and left the room.

Bill tried to diminish the mention of another woman and answered lightly, "Oh, she went back to Midland and married a guy named Charles Black." He hoped he had sounded nonchalant about the whole thing, but inside, he felt another part of his heart shrivel.

For the rest of the evening, Bette was cold and withdrawn, but it was the beginning of a pattern that would continue throughout their marriage. The honeymoon was cut short and they flew back to Austin in silence. Bette returned home to her father to seek an annulment, which never happened, while Bill returned to his military duties at Fort Hood, Texas.

In March of 1956, Bill was given an honorable discharge from the Army. He found a job in the insurance business in Houston and Bette found a teaching position in the Houston schools. Four years after their marriage, Bette became pregnant by artificial insemination, her seventh try, and in January, 1958, gave birth to a son, John Cavan Harris. The Connecticut General Life Insurance Company transferred Bill to Hartford, Connecticut. While Bill was doing reasonably well professionally, his personal life left much to be desired. He had never really loved Bette, at least not the way he had loved Frances and their problems brought on another separation.

Somehow, Bill and Bette resolved their problems and adopted a daughter through private adoption. Irene was only five-days-old when she was placed in their arms in 1962. Then Bill and Bette moved to Fulshear, Texas, a small town to the northwest of Houston, and Bette hated it.

Through it all, Bill never stopped thinking about Frances or what his life might have been like with her. From time to time a friend would say, "Have you heard about Frances?" Of course he hadn't and he waited with a pounding heart with the latest news of her. Now he learned that she had gone back to

163

college to get her degree. He smiled with pride for her.

In 1964, Bill and Bette moved back to Houston. It made Bette happy to be back in *civilization*. Bill only shrugged. If that's all it took to make Bette happy, then he'd do it. They had the children to think about. He knew what it would take to make him happy, but he knew he could never have Frances.

On a Sunday afternoon in 1965, Bill received a phone call from Frances at the Houston airport. It nearly knocked him off his feet.

"I'm on my way to Corpus Christi. We moved there from Kansas and I just called to see how you and the family are doing," she said.

"We're fine," he answered as though talking to a stranger rather than the love of his life. Love of his life she might be, but he had made a promise to another woman, and he had to keep Frances at arm's length. He wondered if that would be possible.

They didn't talk long. He learned that she had had *six* children, all born within the first eight years of her marriage to Charles and that the Pi Phi's had reinstated both girls and returned their pins five years after she had married. Their lives had been ruined over nothing. They said their polite good-byes, hung up the phone, and Bill felt the old wounds in his heart reopen.

Chapter 18

Frances found her first teaching job in Corpus Christi in 1969, and by 1972 had divorced Charles and moved to Austin. Bill had been through a divorce from Mary and had already separated several times from Bette, so he understood at least a little of what she went through. He wished he could be there to comfort her, but with the understanding of her sadness, he also comprehended that she was free. The tough part of all this was that he was not. Then in October of 1972, an odd meeting happened, something that stretched the boundaries of credibility.

Bill had gone to the Texas-Arkansas Football game in Memorial Stadium. Seventy thousand people filled the stadium for the game between these long-time rivals. The loud speakers blared. The bands played. Cheerleaders shouted. People stood and cheered for their team. Vendors snaked their way through the bleachers. In short, organized confusion and a cacophony of noises and smells mixed together to create that unique American entity known as the college football game.

Bill had gone to the game with his Boy Scout troop, about six boys, and so was wearing his Scoutmaster's uniform. As he sat watching the half-time show, he felt a gentle tap on his shoulder. When he looked up, he saw a beautiful, forty-year old woman with a gray streak through her dark hair.

She said, "Aren't you Bill Harris?"

He looked up, heard her voice and shouted, "Frances!" He jumped up, hugged her and started kissing her all over her face. People sitting near them started clapping, embarrassing Frances and she started to pull away.

"How did you ever find me in this crowd?"

"You have to admit you'd be hard to miss," she said with a smile and twinkle of mischief in her eyes. "You're a big guy with red hair and your arms are spread wide to encompass seven seats--your troop I presume."

"Yep, you got me there. I am a bit hard to miss." He pulled her close and started kissing her again. This time she broke free and started to move away from him.

"Wait, Frances. What row are you on?"

"Fifty-two."

Ten minutes later, Bill had dried his eyes, pulled himself together and went up to row 52 to find her. When he spotted her, he reached for her hand and pulled her away from her companion. He took her up to the very top row where they sat. Bill started kissing her again.

Finally, Bill said, "You know, Frances, I've never stopped loving you. I've been married twice, and neither one was a success. There always seemed to be so many problems. Sometimes it was the other person's fault, and honestly, sometimes it was mine. But through it all, I never stopped loving you."

Frances blushed. "Bill, you're embarrassing me."

"Oh, Frances, I'd never want to do that." Then he grew very serious and reached for her hand. "Frances, I know this is 22 years too late, but marry me."

"I can't do that," she said.

"Why not? You're not married anymore."

"But you are," she reminded him. "Besides. . . ." She held up her left hand, and there on her third finger was an engagement ring.

Bill thought he would die right then and there. How could this be happening to him? They had spent 22 years apart hearing only bits and pieces of each others' lives. They had been through marriages and divorces, and truth be told, Bill's own marriage was tottering on the edge of a precipice for the third time in it's rocky life. They could rid of themselves of all past encumbrances and finally have a life together.

Instead of expressing all the thoughts that ran through his brain and the feelings that filled his heart, he took a deep breath and cleared his throat and swallowed hard. "Well, I wish you all the luck in the world."

"Thank you, Bill." She sighed. "Well, the game is almost over and I've got to get back. I came with my younger brother, Roane. He'll think I got lost."

She stood up and he followed suit. "Good-bye, Bill."

"Good-bye, Frances."

They hugged and Bill watched her make her way through the bleachers to an exit. He didn't want to miss a single move. He wanted to be waiting in case she turned to wave. She didn't. Heartbroken once again, he returned to his waiting troop until the game ended.

Bill drove the boys back to Houston and home, just as he

167

knew Frances was on her way home. He didn't understand any of this, except that the fates had a strange sense of humor. They had found each other after all these years, only to say good-bye again. It wasn't fair. None of it was fair. He wondered how he'd get through the rest of his life without his Frances. His Frances? She hadn't been his for a very long time.

Chapter 19

Back at home, Bill and Bette continued their lives, working for the insurance company, loving their children, and growing farther apart. He found the next year very difficult to deal with because his thoughts kept coming back to Frances. He had lost her once to another man and she had borne him six children, whom she loved a great deal. How he wished they had been his red-headed, blue-eyed children, but fate had dealt him another hand and he had to make the best of it. The trouble was, he didn't know if he could anymore.

His children were growing up. He and Bette hardly spoke anymore and when they did, they argued about one thing or another. How he longed for the one thing he could not have, Frances.

In October of 1973, just as things were about to fall apart for good between Bill and Bette, Bill felt he had to do something to see Frances, so he called his unmarried brother.

"Hey, Bob, I was wondering if you'd like a date," Bill began.

"Sure, just don't tell me she has a great personality," he said with a laugh.

"Well she does, but she's also a beautiful woman."

"Sure. Give me her name and number."

The brothers conspired for Bob to ask Frances to attend the Texas-Navy game, but Bill didn't tell his brother that he'd be doing him a favor by giving Bill an excuse to spend the afternoon with Frances in a completely innocent manner. Bob called and Frances accepted his invitation, and together the brothers drove to Austin to take Frances to the football game.

When she opened the door to her little house and saw him standing on her front porch, she squealed, "Bill!"

He gave her a big hug and a kiss, then introduced his brother to her. "I brought something for you." He handed her two bottles of Bola Bardolino.

"Thanks so much. It'll be great with dinner," she said. "Come in. Come in. I'm sure you didn't come all this way to stand outside on the porch." She opened the door wider and led them into her living room.

He looked at the nicely decorated surroundings. "Very nice place you have here." Lord, that sounded so trite, but his mind had gone blank.

"Thank you." Let me give you a tour. She led them through the little two bedroom house and they ended up in the kitchen. "I think dinner's just about ready. I only have to serve."

"Smells great," Bob said sniffing the air.

"A wonderful aroma," Bill concurred.

They enjoyed a wonderful dinner of King Ranch Chicken before going to the game, a game at which Texas led Navy 40 to 0 at the half.

As they left the stadium, Bill asked Frances if she knew of a night club where they had dancing? He figured that holding Frances in his arms would be about as good as hugging her.

"I know just the place," Frances said with a wink, and she guided them to a nice little place downtown.

Bob drank a Tom Collins. He liked it so much he ordered another then promptly put his head down on the table and fell asleep. That gave Bill the perfect opportunity to dance with Frances over and over. She allowed him to hold her close and she snuggled close to him while they moved to the music.

After two hours, Frances noted the time and they woke Bob.

"We've got to get Frances home now," Bill whispered in his brother's ear.

Bob sat up startled. "What?"

"We've got to go," Bill said.

"Oh, yeah."

They left the restaurant and took Frances home. When they arrived at her house, Bob fell asleep again on the sofa in the living room, leaving Bill and Frances alone in the kitchen. Where he took her into his arms.

"So, you didn't marry again," he said matter-of-factly.

Frances shook her head. "No, I didn't really love him. I already made one bad marriage to a man I didn't really love and it was very painful. I didn't want to go through that again."

Bill studied her face. "Frances, why did you marry Charles if you didn't love him?"

She gave a long sigh. "Because I couldn't stand living in the same house with my father anymore. He was mean and vindictive. He kept telling me how much I had disgraced him and the whole family at the University."

"But we didn't do anything wrong!" Bill blurted.

"I know that and you know that, but the rest of the world had their own ideas about what happened and what didn't happen that night in LaGrange. They had their minds made up before we even opened our mouths to speak. I know it wasn't fair. It wasn't right. But it happened a long time ago and there's nothing we can do about it now."

"So you married a man you hardly knew?" Bill asked incredulously.

"Well, yes, but I didn't love him. I certainly wasn't in love with him, but I saw marrying him as a way to get out from under my father."

"And were you happy?"

Frances thought a moment. "No, never really happy. But as time wore on, he got harder and harder to live with. As he grew more successful, he became more overbearing, almost as though he was the only one in the family who knew anything, and he had to make all the decisions. After all, I was just a little housewife. I stayed home and took care of the house and the four kids. What did I know?"

Bill kissed her lightly. "I'm sorry, Frances. It must have been very difficult for you."

She nodded. "But it's over now. What about you?"

"Ah, well, I married someone I really didn't love either, a girl who was already pregnant with another man's child. She tried to pass it off as mine, but I found out. She told me one night and then I went to a couple of doctors and had it confirmed medically. The child couldn't be mine. I'm sterile. Well, I was devastated. We were only married a few months. Then I met Bette.

"I didn't really love her either, but she called me and wrote me letters while I was in the basic training with the Army. She was pretty and we had fun together so we got married. But there was never any great passion between us. We've been separated a couple of times and things are not going well for us now." He held up his hand with a short distance between his thumb and forefinger. "We're this far from calling it quits."

"What about the children?" she asked.

"They're half-grown already. I don't think they'd take the break up too badly. They'll have lives of their own."

Bill and Frances spent three hours in the kitchen, talking, laughing, hugging, kissing, and drinking coffee. Bill looked up at the clock on the wall. "You know, this has been great, but I've got to be getting back."

"I understand," Frances said sweetly.

Bill walked out to the living room to wake his brother. "Bob, we've got to head home. It's one o'clock in the morning."

Bleary-eyed, Bob sat up and looked around for a moment to get his bearings. Realizing where he was he stood to face Frances. "It was really great to meet you, Frances."

"Same here, Bob. Maybe we can do it again sometime."

"I would love to."

Bill drove his brother home to San Marcos, about 30 miles south of Austin, then made his way home to Houston, a happy man. Now he had some indication of what Frances still felt for him. She loved him as much as he loved her. During that drive, he knew what he had to do.

The following Sunday, Bill told Bette that he was going

to file for divorce. Of course she was upset and his children were in tears, but he felt this was his last bid for happiness and he had to grab for it. He packed some of his personal things and went to his mother's house.

The next day, he called Bill Chanslor, an attorney. The two men had played on the same football team while at UT. "Bill, I'd like for you to handle my divorce," he said bluntly.

The attorney expressed his sympathy that Bill's marriage was breaking up, but explained he didn't handle divorces. Instead, he gave his old friend the name of another attorney named Charles who could help him out. Bill immediately called Charles and went to see him. He started divorce proceedings that same day.

Once he had filed for divorce, Bill drove to Austin every Friday afternoon and stayed until Monday. They spent the weekends together having fun, something that Frances's sixteen-year-old daughter Nancy had never seen her mother do.

At first, Bill never intended to spend his nights with Frances at her house because of Nancy, but when Frances requested that he stay, he couldn't resist. Their first night together, they were in Frances's bedroom laughing and giggling. Nancy, whose bedroom was located just across the hall, didn't know how to react to the sounds of her mother having a good time.

She came across the hall and pounded on the door and shouted. "Really! I can't stand all that laughing and talking."

That only caused Bill and Frances to laugh louder and become more boisterous, like little children. Tell children not to do something and you can bet they'll do it.

During their weekend interludes, Bill and Frances went to movies, played tennis, rode bikes, went for walks and went out to dinner. In short, it was a real courtship and they were discovering how much fun they could have together. They even went swimming at Lake Austin, and at Thanksgiving of 1973, Bill took Frances on her first camping trip to Garner State Park on the Frio River.

By this time, Bette's slowness in the divorce was driving them both a little crazy and during the camping trip, they had a terrible scene, shouting and screaming at each other, each one laying blame for the delay on the other. Nearby campers, embarrassed at the highly personal tone of the argument, began packing up and leaving.

Eventually, they realized how silly it all was. Arguing was not going to hurry the divorce in any way shape or form. They tearfully made up and drove back to Austin more in love than ever. Forever afterwards, Bill and Frances would call this trip their "Dear Hunt."

During the spring and early summer, Bill continued his weekend trips to Austin. Since Frances was teaching, he would do her yard work for her. When she came home from school, she'd cook for him. In fact they did everything together. It was really a very happy time for them both. They had everything they needed but the divorce decree.

Chapter 20

Gradually, Bill introduced Frances to his two children. By now, Cavan was 17 and Irene was 13. Cavan was polite and friendly while Irene was openly hostile. However, they had hope that she'd accept this new woman in her father's life given enough time and understanding.

Frances had no problem winning over Bill's mother. For as much as the older woman tried to encourage Bill to go back to his marriage, she had to admit that Frances was beautiful and charming, and might make her son far happier than Bette ever had. Sometimes, Frances drove to Houston for the weekend and stayed with Bill at his mother's house.

And the divorce dragged on. The lawyers weren't doing anything for them and so Bill and Bette had their own private discussions to work things out. It took months but Bill finally realized that the only way to finish this divorce was to allow Bette to dictate the terms. They finally worked out an agreement.

Bette would get everything they owned as well as substantial child support. Bill would get all their debts and an old car. However, several years later, after Bette remarried, she generously returned Bill's family heirlooms to him. In short, Bette would get everything, and Bill would get Frances, but he loved her so much, he would willingly sign everything away but still, no papers had been signed.

In the spring and early summer of 1974, Bill spent more and more time in Austin with Frances. Because of his pending divorce, they kept to themselves and discovered they didn't need anyone else to be happy.

Frances cooked wonderful meals for Bill and Nancy as the summer passed by. They were growing increasingly impatient with Bette and the divorce lawyers but there was nothing they could do about it. Finally, on August 7, 1974, Bill's lawyer called.

"Bill, glad I caught you in," Charles said.

As soon as Bill heard his lawyer's voice he wondered what other legal shenanigans he'd have to deal with now. "What hurdle do I have to jump over now? I've already agreed to everything Bette wanted."

"Relax. The judge signed the papers today. You're a free man."

Bill nearly fainted with surprise and joy. Instead, he let himself sink into a nearby chair. Frances who stood several feet from him walked over to him immediately.

"What is it, Bill?"

"Thanks, Charles.

"The judge signed the papers. The divorce is final."

Frances wept for joy.

"Now we can be married," Bill said. "Happy Birthday."

Frances would never forget this birthday, her forty-third.

Bill walked away from his marriage with his old car and his clothes, into Frances's arms.

Chapter 21

"I can't believe it's finally happened. Now we can get married," Frances said in disbelief.

"But we have to wait 30 days. Texas law requires it."

"I know, but let's see what we can find out."

Bill watched in astonishment as Frances called the Secretary of States' offices in New Mexico, Colorado, Oklahoma, Arkansas, and Louisiana.

When she got off the phone she said, "We can get married tomorrow in Louisiana."

Although they had been watching TV coverage of Richard Nixon resigning the presidency, they immediately left Austin and headed to Lake Charles, Louisiana. On their way, Bill realized something.

"Frances, we don't have any rings."

She snuggled closer to him in the car. "That's okay, I don't need any ring. We've already waited too long."

"No," he said adamantly. I'm not going to get married without rings. We'll be passing through Houston. We can get them there."

"But it'll be night and everything will be closed," Frances said.

"I'm sure we can find an all night jewelry store. It's a big city."

When they got to Houston, they drove all over the city looking for a jewelry shop with its open sign still lit. The closest they came was an all night pawnshop. Lacking any other choices, they went inside and bought two rings, then hit the road again.

They arrived in Lake Charles the next morning, August 8, 1974 at 9 a.m. They found the marriage license office and filed the papers, then found a lab that would do their blood test and give them immediate results. Their last stop was an Episcopal Church where the minister did the honors and performed the marriage. Frances's son, Jim Black, met them and served as a witness in the ceremony.

The next day, Bill and Frances drove back to Austin and attended a huge DKE party on a riverboat on Lake Austin, and Bill approached the captain.

"Captain, tell me, do you have the power to perform marriage ceremonies?"

The captain, having had a little too much to drink, tottered on his feet a bit before answering. "But of course.

"Then would you marry me to this beautiful woman please?"

"Would love to."

The captain barely made it through the ceremony and then declared, "By the power invested in me by the state of. . . where am I?. . .oh, yes, Texas, I declare you husband and wife. But only for the duration of the cruise."

The crowd of 100 or more DKEs cheered wildly and Bill kissed his bride.

The next day, Bill and Frances started packing up her

house to move her to Houston. They had rented a new three-bedroom condo called Madison Place on Richmond at Kirby. Frances secured a teaching position with Pasadena ISD (Independent School District) and then later with Houston ISD. Bill went back to Southwestern Life Insurance Company and became a huge success selling tax deferred investments all over the Houston area, particularly with the Deer Park ISD, Galena Park ISD, and La Marque ISD near Galveston. They lived in Madison Place for a year then bought a pretty little story and a half on Vassar. They assumed the mortgage and paid $90,000.

One Sunday in 1975, something happened that would change their life. They were out riding in the country and stopped to read the historical markers. One particular marker in the town of Industry, Texas caught his eye and Bill stopped to read it. He immediately recognized the name of Charles Fordtran and the story that went with it. He took a picture of the marker and showed his mother.

"Mother, am I related to this man?" he asked.

She looked at the picture then up at her son. "You Silly Billy, of course you are. He's your great-great-grandfather."

In that moment, he realized that his roots on his mother's side of the family were in Austin and Fayette County. Then shortly after that, Miss Ima Hogg called Bill's mother and invited her to come to the dedication of her great-grandfather's house at Winedale, about three miles outside of Round Top, Texas.

Bill, Frances, his brother Bob, Bob's wife Peggy, and their mother drove out to Round Top for the event. After the ceremony, they decided to find a place to eat in Round Top and found the Birklebach Café. The town was deserted and they were the only people in the little restaurant.

When the five travelers had found a table, a woman came from behind the counter. Before she could say anything, Bill asked, "May we have five menus please?"

In a very thick German accent she answered, "Vell, ve don't haf any menus. Vat ve haf is a Cherman plate lunch."

Bill clapped his hand together. "Fine. Then we'll have five German plate lunches."

Within minutes, the woman brought out plates piled high with sauerkraut, link sausage, German potato salad, and canned peaches. She finished serving by placing an unopened loaf of bread in the center of the table.

They thanked the woman and when she walked away, Bill turned to Frances. "I think I want to live in Round Top."

Bill's mother gasped. "You can't be serious!"

"Frances, could you be happy in Round Top?"

She gave him a brilliant smile. "I'd love to live in Round Top."

They sought out a Real Estate agent and found Annie Schatte. They began researching farm and ranch ads in the Houston papers, and two months later Annie called saying she had some farms to show them. They made an appointment to go to Round Top to see them.

Annie couldn't meet them but she sent her son Odis. He took them from farm to farm and they loved them all, but lacked the required down payment, until they came to the farm of Mr. Hatch.

"Well, what do you think of it?" Mr. Hatch asked. "It's got fifty-four acres, a good patch of land."

"We love it, Mr. Hatch, but I don't think we could come up with the down payment," Bill confided.

Mr. Hatch rubbed his chin in thought. "Tell you what. You don't need a down payment. It's got 54 acres and I'll let it go for $54,000. I'll carry the note for 10 years at 8 per cent simple interest, and you make one annual payment. How does that sound?"

Bill and Frances looked at each other in astonishment then quickly agreed to Mr. Hatch's proposal.

They closed on the property in November 1977 and spent that first weekend in the only building on the farm, a falling down log cabin of only one room. As they examined this new possession more carefully, Bill noticed something burned into the wall above the door.

"Frances, look at that."

She stood by his side and saw what looked to be the handiwork of someone adept with a branding iron.

They stood with their arms around each other looking at the little sign.

"Honey, why don't we name our little farm 'Heart of My Heart?"

"I'd love it."

For the next eight years, between 1977 and 1985, they spent every weekend at their little hideaway in the woods.

Chapter 22

The first winter in their little cabin was bitterly cold. Only occasionally used by its former owners as a deer lease, it was not made for winter use. Wind blew in between missing chinks in the logs, under the floorboards and around the windows, so much so that the curtains would wave in the breeze. Their only heat came from a pot bellied wood stove in front of what had been a fireplace at one time. Frances decided the first thing she should do was to block up all the holes and seal the cabin up as tightly as possible. It helped a lot but the temperature inside was still colder than outside.

One such night, Bill returned to bed from a trip to the bathroom. As he got into bed he gave Frances an idea just how cold it was.

"The water in the toilet was frozen," he said with a chuckle.

On another night, Bill got up to stoke the stove, but the last log was an inch too long, so Bill gave it a hefty shove and pushed the stove from the stove pipe. Flames leaped from the hole.

"Fire! Frances! Fire!"

Frances scurried to Bill's side just as the black, hot, stove pipes fell from the ceiling. Thinking fast, she grabbed a lid from one of her pots and literally put a lid on the flames. Dark smoke filled the cabin. They both started to cough and Bill rushed to open the door.

"I don't know what's worse," Frances said between coughs. "The smoke or the cold air."

They stood huddled together at the door, blankets wrapped around them, taking in huge gulps of fresh air while they shivered.

"Bill, something's got to be done. We can't go on like this. Freezing. Breathing in that horrible smoke."

"I know. I know. We'll think of something," he assured her.

The smoke cleared and the pipe cooled enough for Bill to put the stove back in its spot and hook it back up to the stovepipe. They spent the rest of the night in bed with their two Labrador retrievers to help keep them warm. The next week, they bought electric blankets and survived the winter very nicely.

Because the cabin was nowhere near air tight, Bill and Frances found it impossible to keep insects out, particularly wasps. They had a collection of different colors of wasps: black, brown, blue, yellow, and those horrible red hornets. The wasps built nests all over the cabin and they went in and out all day for another load of mud. It seemed that they would form up in a cloud by the screen door and wait to be let out.

Bill remembers on one particular Saturday afternoon while he was trying to take a nap, the wasps refused to let him sleep. He had to get up more than once to open the screen door to temporarily clear the cabin. Apparently, they could get in on their own but needed help getting out for more mud.

The red hornets, on the other hand were a different matter. They lived in holes in the ground and would come flying out with a vengeance. They had attitude.

One day, Frances told their friend and neighbor, Leon Hale, a columnist with a Houston newspaper, that she had gone to a party, felt a lump in her dress and it turned out to be a mud dauber's nest. He wrote a cute story about it in his column.

The only tractor Bill ever had at the ranch is now fifty years old, a small garden tractor with a shredder and a cultivator. He calls it the *Old Red Mule*. He bought it from Mr. Hatch for $250, and considers it the best buy he ever made.

He can pull a shredder or a bush hog with it. He can pull a disc to row up a garden, and he has a cultivator to actually row it up and take care of the rows the first month of the garden. It runs like a top thanks to an old German, Mr. Bergman, who happens to be a genius at tractor maintenance.

Those early years at the farm were very hard. They had no extra money because they were still maintaining their home in Houston, had had six children in college, but they put plenty of sweat equity into the place.

One Christmas, Bill wanted to give Frances something really pretty for Christmas, but sorrowed at the dearth of cash. He thought and thought and finally in desperation made up a hand drawn IOU.

I promise Frances that I will someday give her a big beautiful Victorian house.

That was a promise Bill worked hard to keep.

185

When spring came, Bill plowed a plot of ground for a vegetable garden. Frances had never had a garden but she enthusiastically embraced the idea. She bought flats of plants and spent the weekend planting them in neat rows. When they returned the following week, they stared in horror at what they found.

"Oh, no, Bill. They're all gone! All the plants are gone!"

The deer had eaten every one of their tender seedlings.

"Well, we're not going to let a few deer outsmart us," Bill declared. "We want a garden and we'll have one, deer or no deer."

The next weekend when they returned, they came armed with his and hers chainsaws, chicken wire, and a drop auger to dig post holes. Together, they cut down cedar trees, made fence posts, set the posts, and ran the chicken wire around the perimeter of a large garden. Then Frances planted her seeds.

"Bill, I've just finished planting four rows of squash," she announced proudly.

He looked at her dubiously. "You mean four hills of squash, don't you?"

She shook her head. "No, four rows. Squash is my favorite vegetable."

"I certainly hope so because that's enough squash to feed the entire county."

As it turned out, he was right. She also planted 64 tomato plants and harvested them by the wheelbarrow full. Bill suggested they put up a produce stand by the side of the road, but instead opted to give them to his insurance clients all summer. In time, they also had chickens and eggs, cattle, pigs, a small herd of sheep, a huge fruit orchard and berry bushes.

While Frances tended her garden, Bill planted his pecan orchard. First, he planted a dozen trees, all six to eight feet tall. He dug the holes himself and planted them carefully near the cabin and gave them plenty of water on each of his weekend visits. But despite his best efforts, all of his trees died. The next winter, Bill bought an additional 35 trees and hired someone with a posthole digger to plant them down near the creek where native pecans were growing.

To ensure they got plenty of water, he bought a 300 gallon water trailer, hooked it up to his little 40-year-old tractor and started down the steep, narrow, winding road to the bottom meadow. The heavy water trailer started pushing the little tractor, and as the whole thing gathered momentum and speed, Bill struggled to hang on to the steering wheel, all the while trying to keep the tractor from turning over. He watered the trees and repeated the harrowing trip down the hill each week but to no avail. All but a few of the trees died.

Discouraged but still determined to have a pecan orchard, he said, "Frances, let's do it like the squirrels. We'll plant nuts instead of trees and maybe they'll adapt to conditions as they grow."

Carefully, he laid out four rows with stakes and string all across the meadow. He used the tines of a pitchfork to make four deep holes at a time, then he dropped a nut into each hole, covered the nuts, and moved down ten yards to do it again.

That winter and spring they enjoyed unusually good rainfall and the nuts germinated and grew. They ended up with four rows of hundreds of little pecan trees about 18" tall by fall. Bill was elated with his long-awaited success.

That fall, Bill's teenage daughter, Irene, had a boyfriend, Vince, who wanted to go deer hunting and Bill and Frances agreed that they could stay at the ranch for the weekend and hunt. Frances and Bill left Houston a little later than usual, so when they arrived at the ranch, his daughter and her boyfriend had already arrived.

When they drove up to the little cabin, Vince came out smiling broadly. He extended his hand in greeting and said, "Hello, Mr. Harris, I went down to check out the deer stand in the bottom meadow and the weeds were so tall we couldn't see the deer very well so I hooked up the shredder and mowed the bottom meadow for you."

He had mowed down every little tree. Bill gulped. "Thanks, Vince." He walked away but his spirit was broken. Perhaps some things just aren't meant to be and Bill gave up on pecan trees.

Chapter 23

Before long, Bill and Frances discovered that it would not be easy to attract their children to the ranch for a visit. After all, there was nothing to do and they only had a "crummy old cabin" to stay in with no heating or air conditioning. Bill's 14-year-old daughter Irene said she'd only come if she could have a horse, and that began the acquisition of a variety of farm animals.

Ever the indulgent dad, Bill fenced a pasture then located a gentle little mare by the name of *Star*. She would come when called by name and loved to drink orange sodas. She also loved to stand in the small pond and stamp her front foot to splash water up on her belly. Irene spent about five irregular weekends at the ranch then lost interest in the horse. Bill sold Star back to her previous owner for the same price he had paid--$300.

Their next animal adventure came in the form of *Little Darling,* a pig. A friend from Houston called one day and said, "Bill, do you have room for a pig out at your ranch?"

Bill thought that an odd way to begin a phone conversation, but said, "Sure, we have room for one little pig." Then promptly went to pick up Little Darling.

She turned out to be a half-grown Poland/China black and

white pig. The previous owner had kept her in the house, had let her ride in the front seat of the car and root around in her flowerbeds. He told Little Darling's owner that he would drive her home in the back of his small VW pickup.

She took one look and saw two black lab puppies, each about one-third the size of Little Darling and terrified of the pig, and said, "Oh, oh, let's put her in a box."

The woman cut air holes and tied the box closed with white cotton twine and after much crying, lamentation, and gnashing of teeth, the woman finally let Bill drive away and leave her behind. He honestly wondered why, if the woman loved her little pig so much, she wanted to get rid of her, but one look at the shambles in her yard explained it.

In the time it took to drive a block, the pig had burst from the box, tore up the cotton string and was terrorizing the two puppies. It was noon on Friday and the traffic on West Loop was terrible. When he reached the ramp to join the Katy Freeway to head west, the pig was standing up on a wheel well looking out and watching the heavy traffic.

Bill pulled over to the side of the road so the hundreds of cars could get by and every car that went by would toot the horn twice as if to tell him that he had a *pig loose in the back of the truck!* Needless to say, Bill found the trip along the crowded freeway most harrowing.

When he reached Sealy, he pulled into a little place to get a beer. He was at the counter, when two teenaged boys ran in and shouted, "Mister, is that your pig running down main street?"

Bill immediately dropped the beer and ran after Little Darling as fast as he could. The problem was, she could run faster. Finally, in desperation, he stopped and called out in a loud voice, "Here, Little Darling!"

After calling for her several times, the little pig stopped, turned around and returned to him. He promptly picked her up and put her back in the truck. He put the two lab puppies in the front seat of the truck and took off their collars and leashes, and putting them together, placed them around the neck of the pig, and it was still a tight fit.

Then he opened the rear window of the truck and drove the rest of the way to Round Top with the pig pulled up against the rear of the cab. Meanwhile the labs had never been in the front seat before and they spent the rest of the trip climbing all over Bill and kissing him. By the time he reached the farm, he was exhausted. The good farmers of Sealy still talk about the crazy man from Houston who called his pig Little Darling. Bill and Frances raised Little Darling until she reached a whopping 275 pounds, then took her to the meat market and had her butchered for bacon, pork chops and ground pork.

Bill and Frances learned a lot about hogs with Little Darling. One main thing they found out is that they won't stay in a pigpen by themselves. One way or another, Little Darling would get out to graze with their herd of cows, if you could call three a herd.

For the next five years, Heart of My Heart Ranch was home to two pigs a year, which eventually filled their freezer. Bill took the pigs to the market each November when they weighed in at approximately 300 pounds, and getting them to market was almost as monumental as getting that first pig to the farm.

Bill would have to walk the pigs through several traps into the cattle pen, then down the cattle chute and into the back end of the cattle trailer. Somehow during this process the pigs would realize that this was a one-way trip and they would resist getting in the trailer. No amount of pulling and pleading can get a 300 pound pig into the trailer if she doesn't want to go. These last day adventures got worse and worse.

The final straw was the last pig. Bill got her into the chute up to the last step up when she lay down and would not get up. Bill's helper, a strong Mexican worker named Johnny Tovar, helped him for the next hour, tying to get that pig into the trailer. Finally, Bill sent Johnny to get a come-along.

They put a steel cable around the pig's neck and began to winch the pig into the trailer. The cable got tighter and tighter around the pig's neck until it cut off the air supply and the pig slumped unconscious near death.

Bill shouted, "Pull that cable off the pig."

Still, the pig did not breath.

He rolled the pig over on her back, not an easy feat considering she was not only 300 pounds, but unconscious as well, then he jumped on her and began pumping air into her chest. The pig still didn't breathe.

"Johnny, blow into the pig's mouth," Bill suggested.

"Who me?" Johnny asked incredulously.

"Yes, and blow hard."

Johnny shrugged his shoulders and began blowing air into the pig's mouth while Bill pumped her chest. In less than a minute, she began to breathe. Bill and Johnny rolled the pig over on her stomach, but she was groggy and would not stand up. They pushed and shoved but were unable to get her into the trailer.

Bill had read somewhere in his pig book that the ear was the most tender place on the pig's body, so when nothing else worked he instructed Johnny on what to do. "Bite her on the ear."

Johnny looked at Bill. "Who me?"

"Bite her, Johnny. Bite hard."

Johnny rolled his eyes, crossed himself, then bit the pig's ear hard. The pig screamed in pain, jumped up and ran into the trailer to put distance between herself and these crazy fiends.

With that, Johnny said, "I quit," and walked away.

He never came back and those were the last pigs Bill raised. It really didn't save any money and it was getting to be too much trouble, but Bill and Frances loved having animals on the farm, so they decided to nurture their small herd of cattle. Bill started raising registered Santa Gertrudis cattle.

Then one day while driving in Deer Park on a country road, Bill saw a sign advertising Spanish goats. He stopped and bought two young goats one gray and one white. He put them in the back of the van and took off for the farm. They were cute little goats that grew up to be pretty but a lot of trouble. He didn't have a real pen to put them in so he put them in the back yard behind the log cabin.

One Friday when Bill and Frances arrived from the city, they found the goats had pushed in a screen, climbed into the log cabin, lived there for a few days, and tore up the cabin. Goat droppings were everywhere.

At first they acted so glad to see company until Frances reached for her broom and started screaming at them. The last straw came when they ruined a young fruit tree orchard by pushing the trees down and eating the tops out.

Goats are cute but very mischievous. They can jump up on top of everything including autos with expensive paint jobs. Bill never said exactly how they died, but they eventually found their way into his barbecue pit.

Bill conducted another experiment in animal husbandry with sheep. One cold winter night when Bill was in Houston and Frances was out at the ranch alone, she heard a mother sheep, who had tiny twins, bleating and running up and down a fence by the pig waller.

Frances took a flashlight and saw that one of the lambs had fallen into the frozen water and had only its head sticking out. She donned her rubber boots and waded into the terrible smelling cold mud and pulled the baby out. She called the vet and explained what had happened.

"Dry it off then put it in the oven at its lowest setting, give it some warm milk and keep it warm."

She did as the vet had told her and when Bill came the next day, he found the baby lamb sitting in Frances's lap having a bottle. "What have we here?" he asked.

Frances explained what had happened and that she had spent the rest of the night in their bed snuggling with the little lamb to keep it warm.

When they tried to reunite mother and baby, mother would have nothing to do with the helpless little creature because it smelled like the pig waller, so Bill built a tiny pen and put the mother and both her babies in the pen. Finally, the mother took it back and both grew up healthy.

Because of the terrible summer heat in Texas the sheep

must be sheared every June. Grown sheep weigh about 125 pounds and don't want to be sheared. Bill would tackle a sheep and throw him on his back, sit on him to hold him down while Frances clipped away with the electric shears he had bought her. The idea was to clip the entire sheep and end up with one complete hide all connected. Then they'd stuff the wool in a feedbag and sell it at a local feed store for $10.00 a bag.

Finally, Bill hired a hand, Doug, who had grown up on a sheep ranch at San Angelo who could shear the sheep by himself in a few seconds. Once, they left the ranch for the day and left him in charge of shearing their huge herd of six sheep. When they came back they found him drunk and the sheep sheared in all kinds of exotic cuts---a Mohawk--a lion's ruff--a poodle cut.

Bill pushed back the hat on his head because he didn't believe what he was seeing. Frances just looked at him incredulously. Finally, she said, "Doug, what are you doing to the sheep?"

"Aw, Ms. Harris, they looks so purdee," he slurred.

Doug stayed on for a short time but when his drinking got out of hand, they reluctantly let him go. When Doug left Bill's employ, he decided that he and Frances were too old to be wrestling sheep and reluctantly gave up raising them.

Later, they heard Doug found employment at a power plant as a welder's helper. One day he fell 70 feet from a smokestack and nearly killed himself. He recovered and still occasionally visits Bill and Frances with something to sell like shrimp or firewood.

For many years, Bill and Frances kept a large and

successful poultry barn and pen. But the first ducks they got before the poultry barn was built were raised on their small pond along with a few beautiful geese that would swim along side and eat water plants from their hands when they floated by in tubes on the pond.

When they arrived on Friday afternoon, the ducks knew that if they came up to the cabin Bill would feed them corn. Bill would call to them and they would waddle up single file and he would feed them. As the lab puppies grew up they started chasing and harassing the ducks so that eventually they moved over to the neighbor's ponds, but when they heard our little diesel VW pick up arrive, they'd fly over, land on the pond and march up for their corn supper.

One weekend Bob, Bill's brother and several friends were helping him put a tin roof on a barn he built. When Bill saw the ducks flying over the barn he called out, "Hey, you ducks, if you land on the pond and come on up here, I'll give you some corn." Of course he knew that is what they were going to do but the other men looked at him in astonishment when the ducks appeared to obey his suggestion.

When it came to the chickens, Frances decided she wanted to raise a variety. Of course she wanted to raise the big beautiful Rhode Island Reds as well as the black and white Plymouth Rock and white leghorns chickens. They were good layers and were great fryers. But she also wanted to raise exotic varieties such as the silks, Polish top notch, banties and others.

So Bill and Frances bought two-dozen three-day-old chicks, took them to Houston and raised them in their small green house until they were old enough to live on their own at the farm. When they were big enough, Bill put them in a cardboard box in the back of his van and began the trip to Round Top.

It was a hot summer day and Bill didn't think the temperature would have any effect on the chicks, but he finally realized the heat inside that box was detrimental to them when he stopped for gas in Bellville. While pumping gas he peeked in at the chicks and saw that they were dying. Some had already expired, lying on their backs with their feet up in the air.

Bill was frantic. "Help! Does anyone know what to do for dying chickens?"

A man, who looked like a farmer, came over for a look. "Quick blow in their mouths and get some water."

Together they blew and sprinkled and got the chicks up on their feet if somewhat wobbly.

"If I was you, I'd take these chicks out of the box and put them in the cab with you. Turn on the AC and let them run around in the cool air."

Bill thanked the man for his advice and did as he suggested. For the rest of the trip Bill had little chicks perching on his shoulder, flitting from front to back seat, and causing general havoc in his van. When he got to Round Top, he took them to Mrs. Morrow to nurse them back to health.

Mrs. Morrow was a dear little unsophisticated country German woman who had plain old chickens. She was amazed when these chickens grew up with topnotch, feathered feet and long silky feathers and laid blue eggs. Bill gave her half the chickens for taking care of them for him until his pen was finished.

Bill continued to thrive in his business and became a highly sought after life insurance agent, easily tripling his income. Frances continued teaching school, and she began designing her dream house for their hideaway in her mind. By 1983, they realized that their hearts and their minds were always in Round Top and they wanted to live there permanently, and decided the time was right to sell their Houston home and build their dream house on the ranch.

Chapter 24

In the past few years, Frances had gotten her insurance license and had been working in Bill's office. Now, living in Round Top, she found a job teaching school at the Round Top Elementary School. She moved into the little cabin and began designing their dream home in earnest.

Bill split his time between Houston and Round Top, spending two or three nights a week with his mother taking care of her and attending to his prospering insurance business. But every Thursday night, he drove out to Round Top to be with Frances for the next several days. Fortunately, they sold their Houston home quickly and had the cash they needed to finish paying off the ranch and build their new house.

In 1984, Bill went to the county Soil Conservation Service office in LaGrange to investigate what he would need to do to put in a pond, specifically the rules and regulations. He talked with a civil engineer from LaGrange, a Mr. Koenig. Bill quickly discovered that he had a soil conservation problem, and under certain conditions, they would help Bill pay half the cost of the pond while he paid the other. It was all part of a Department of Agriculture program to help farmers conserve their topsoil.

A month or so later the pond was approved and Bill contacted a Mr. Fricke, to operate a D7 dozer to dig a three-acre pond. Two great things happened as a result of him digging out the 5000 cubic yards of dirt for the pond.

First, he had to take forty post oak trees down from the pond site. Bill had the trees cut into ten cords of oak firewood and 3,000 board feet of lumber, 1x2s, 2x4s, and 4x6s. Later, Bill used the lumber to build barns, gates and other outbuildings on the farm.

The second lucky break came when the bulldozer operator had to move 3500 cubic yards of gravel out of the pit because it would cause the dam to leak. He made a mountain of gravel on the far side of the lake. Frances thought it was ugly so Bill called a gravel company and Bill sold them the 3,500 cubic yards of gravel for $1.35 a yard which was enough to pay his half of the cost to build the pond and pay for all the labor to cut up the oak trees. All in all, the lake was free to Bill and has been a great place to swim, fish, and boat for the past twenty years.

All this time, Frances was happily working on her house plans. Each week Bill and Frances discussed her house design and Bill was pleased that it made Frances so happy to work on her beautiful Victorian home. She designed it specifically to showcase the beautiful furniture and art collections they had inherited from their grandparents.

When the plans were just as they wanted them, Bill found a local builder, Eddie Pilcek from Industry, Texas to make her plans a reality. In less than four months, their beautiful house was built, complete with a 2,000 square foot covered porch. They had sold their house in Houston for a handsome profit and settled into Round Top for good.

Some seven years after Bill had given Frances that IOU at Christmas, Bill did in fact give Frances a huge, two-story Victorian house free and clear. When they moved in, she dug around in her purse and found the old IOU.

As she handed it to him she said, "Consider it paid."

But no matter how wonderful the new house, neither of them will ever forget the eight years spent in the log cabin, the cozy fires in the new chimney, the nights snuggled down in the flannel sheets under a goose down comforter and the nude swims in the small pond with the dogs, ducks and geese.

Of all their animals, they consider their most important, particularly after they started their bed and breakfast, their dogs. For many years they had three black labs, but in 2001, they have golden retriever triplets named Larry, Curly and Mo, and they are working dogs.

Their main duty has been to greet guests and escort them around the property on hikes. They have entertained the visiting children for endless hours. They have all been water dogs taking daily swims in the lake, diving for sinking objects thrown by the guest, sitting for long hours at Bill's feet.

The only non retriever on the ranch was a wonderful Basset hound, Mac, who would run in figure eights out of sheer delight, bay and howl as only a hound can, and take long naps. When too tired to raise his head, he always thumps his tail to greet new arrivals. And all the dogs have had sweet, patient dispositions.

One bride wrote, "Mr. Harris gave me away and the lovely labs were my attendants."

They loved their beautiful new house and frequently

201

entertained friends and family while continuing to make constant improvements to the farm. They became active participants of Festival Hill, served on the Winedale Council, Frances served as president twice of the women's DYD Club (Do Your Duty Club), and Bill opened a small office in town. They felt at home and accepted by the old time residents and by their many Houston friends with weekend places around Round Top. Life was good.

Chapter 25

Living in Round Top was a far different world than living in Houston, and far different than either of them had ever expected. And as any other small town, the local residents are largely responsible for the character of the town.

Bill and Frances took possession of the cabin on the 2nd weekend of November in 1977. They were ecstatic and on the first night noticed the branding iron burn on the wall by the front door. It read *Heart o Heart.*

"Frances, look at this burn. Let's call our place 'Heart of my Heart!'"

She loved it and the name stuck.

The cabin itself was very primitive, almost no plumbing or electricity and of course the only heat came from a little pot bellied stove. The only ventilation came though the door and windows and one old, noisy, greasy ceiling fan.

The cabin dated back to 1836 and the early inhabitants had fought Indians from the cabin. The chinking between the logs had never been redone and when the wind blew the curtains blew too. They found it bitter cold in the winter and beastly hot in the summer but they had each other and nothing else mattered.

They would sit out on the front porch by the hour and plan the rest of their lives. It was a very happy time for both of them even though they had so much work to do they didn't know where to start.

A kindly neighbor, Otto Hinze was the most helpful. He was a bachelor and lived alone and was about 10-15 years younger than Bill and Frances. He had been born in the cabin and knew the history and was a storehouse of helpful information. He had an old tractor with a posthole digger and he gave Bill lessons in how to do farm work.

He was always available to come help with their many problems. He has since married but still lives close by and they are very good friends.

At one time, Round Top was full of old German farmers who are mostly gone now. To name a few, the mayor of Round Top was a prince of a guy named Don Nagle. He and his wife Lydia were wonderful people. Don was retired and ran a tiny chain saw and lawn mower repair shop.

One day Bill took his chain saw in for minor repairs and Don worked on it for an hour and put in a new spark plug.

When he finished he said, "Okay, two dollars."

Bill looked at him disbelievingly. "Don, you can't charge me $2.00 for this job."

He nodded. "Okay, one dollar."

Bill reached for his wallet and handed him a five-dollar bill.

Don looked at it and said, "Wait a minute, I'll get your change."

"No, Don, you don't understand, I'm paying five dollars."

"Well, gee, it's not a five dollar job," he protested.

"Good, but take it anyway," Bill insisted.

Another time, Frances took her weed eater for a minor repair. Don changed the oil and filled up her gallon gas can with gas and six ounces of oil, the proper mix for her equipment. The oil came in eight-ounce cans but Don prorated the price of the can of oil. He wouldn't charge for eight ounces if she only needed six. What a guy. They don't come like that anymore.

Bill rented a small office from Don which he opened on Saturday mornings and did a little insurance business with the locals. If Don didn't see enough people come to the office he would offer to lower the rent for that month.

Don's wife Lydia enjoyed the reputation of best gardener in Fayette County. She kept a large vegetable and flower garden in her front yard that people from all over Fayette County would come to see.

Another person of note was the local Realtor, Annie Shatte. She helped Bill and Frances find and buy their property. She had lived in Round Top forever, knew everyone, their parents, all their friends and relatives, and was generous to a fault.

In a small town like Round Top with no water system, the local volunteer fire dept is very important. When the town had a yearly fundraiser for the Fire Department, Annie was always the biggest contributor. She was a real character, could cuss like a sailor and was a leading citizen and lived to be nearly 80.

Two other citizens of Round Top were Delphin and Rosalie Hinze, both of German descent. Bill and Frances saw

205

them everywhere around town and they always hugged and kissed the couple when they met. Delphine carved a stew pot stirrer out of cedar for Bill, which he still treasures.

Bill's favorite story about them involves a duck plucking party they had. They had invited Bill and Frances to the party and since Bill's mother was visiting, they took her along. They went to the party at two in the afternoon, and 20 to 30 guests had already arrived. They were sitting in the back yard in a big tight circle.

In the center of the circle sat a big fire and a huge cauldron of boiling water hanging over the fire. They saw a huge gunnysack of live domestic ducks near the fire, big, brightly colored muscovey ducks. Bobby Wagner, a guest, reached into the bag, pulled out one live squawking duck and cut off his head with a small ax! Quick as a flash, he plunged the duck into the boiling water and stepped back.

All hell broke loose when the headless duck popped up out of the boiling water and took off at full speed running around the circle. All the men kicked at the duck but it kept running, bumping into things until it bled to death and collapsed. Bill's mother was horrified! After all the ducks had been killed, Bobby distributed them to everyone and the plucking started. Bill plucked his and helped his mother with her duck.

Then the ducks were cleaned inside and out and put on the pit to cook over a slow oak fire. After slow roasting for two hours, everyone sat down to duck dinner, and when it was acceptable, the trio left for home. Delphine gave Bill two live ducks to take home and he added them to his pond. Rosalee and Delphine are in rest homes now unable to communicate with old friends.

Bill also related another story about them. One day, while he was in his little office on the square, Rosalee and Delphine came to see him.

"Good morning. Good to see you. How can I help you?" he asked as Rosalee moved to hug him. Then Delphine followed suit.

"Please, have a seat." He gestured to the chairs by his desk.

Rosalee said, "We want you to help us?"

Bill cocked his head. "Sure, how?"

Without a word, they started pulling cash out of every pocket, thousands of dollars in bills of all sizes, $4,000 in all.

He jumped up from his seat. "Stop. What are you doing?" What do you want me to do with all this money?"
Delphine said, "We want you to put it someplace safe."

"Okay, okay. Come with me." Bill said. "Let's gather it all up and take it across the street."

Together, they gathered all the bills and walked across the street to the Round Top State bank where they bought some certified checks which Bill sent to an insurance company to buy annuities for them. Bill will always remember Rosalee and Delphine as warm, loving senior citizens.

Another local character that bears mentioning was Butch Schwarz. Bill and Frances bought their first few cows from him, and Frances watched in awe as one of the cows gave birth. When she looked more closely at the little calf, she ran and called Butch in a panic.

"Butch, one of the calves has this odd, hairy thing

hanging down out of his stomach."

"Sounds like a rupture," Butch responded. "I'll come take a look. I'll be right over."

Five minutes later, Butch drove up took one look at the little calf and broke into hysterical laughter.

"What's so funny?" Frances asked.

When Butch finally caught his breath he said, "That's his penis," and he got back in his truck and drove off.

There is really no end to the wonderful people Bill and Frances met during those early years in Round Top. Bill calls them the salt of the earth and loved them dearly. Now at age 70, Bill and Frances feel they're the old characters in town and are not sure they can compare with the generation that came before. They relied on them so much for their lessons in ranch living.

They were so terrible in not knowing how to do anything that after the first few years Bill said to Frances, "As best as I can tell, our failure rate is running at 90 percent. We have to do it wrong, go to town for advice, do it over and finally get it right." But they eventually learned.

That brought to mind another wonderful Round Top experience, one that happened at the Carmine Lumber Yard. In the 70s and early 80s it was owned and operated by three old men from Carmine. One drove the delivery truck, one ran the office and the third operated the lumberyard. One day, while talking to the inside man, Bill told him he needed to build a barn.

"What size?" he asked.

Bill shrugged his shoulders. "I don't know. I just figured a barn was a barn."

"Well, to hold how many square bales?" the man asked.

"I don't know," Bill responded again.

He put pencil to paper and finally looked up at his customer. "I'd say you need a 24' x 24' pole barn to hold 500 square bales." He drew a crude picture on the back of his bill and called it a *plan*. "You go home now and cut down twelve large trees, line them up in two rows exactly 24 feet apart and dig 12 holes five-feet deep. Cut off the tops of the trees so that you leave exactly twelve feet left standing above ground level." Then he cut all the lumber to fit including the trusses and sent a $700 load of cut lumber. The truck driver unloaded the lumber and drove off.

In short order, Bill had twelve poles sticking out of the ground at crazy angles and a pile of new #2 southern yellow pine 2x4s and 2x6s and some 2x12 plates. "What's a plate?" he asked Frances. She just shrugged and walked away.

Bill went back to the lumberyard for some more help. Slowly, and with more instruction, Bill and Frances constructed the barn, carefully following the instructions from the nice man in Carmine.

They did, however, have one major problem they failed to consider: cedar trees get smaller in diameter as they get closer to the top. At the bottom of the hole, the trees were ten inches in diameter, while at 15 feet, they were only half that, which meant that the distance between the top of the two rows of poles was about a foot more then the 24 foot length of the trusses. So when Bill sat the end of a truss on one side, the other end wouldn't reach the plate, 25 feet away. Now what?

He couldn't afford to order new trusses, and he couldn't use the ones he had. Bill wanted to sit down and cry. There was no way he was going to dig up the poles and move them closer. It was a major disaster. Finally, late one Sunday afternoon, Bill called a friend, a Greek architect, whom he asked to stop by the ranch on his way home.

He came by to take a look and then got out his tape measure. He measured and measured and then finally said, "Bill, this isn't even close enough for government work. Go get me your come-along and a 30-foot chain."

Luckily Bill had what he wanted. The architect put the chain across the middle of the 25-foot distance and then took the come-along and winched the two walls together one click at a time. After a couple of inches the poles and plates began to groan and creak. He was literally bending the poles on each side to close the gap enough to use the trusses. Finally he said, "That ought to do it. Bill, get up there and nail in some 45 degree braces to keep what we got."

As instructed, Bill cut some 2x6s about three feet long, then climbed up in each corner of the barn and nailed them in. Then they set the trusses up on the plates that were now 24 feet apart and nailed them in. Now for the moment of truth.

He went up to the come-along and began to open it up one click at a time, an inch a click. The timbers and poles began to moan and creak and shift but they held together. They put the roof on, hung some huge doors, and now nearly 20 years later the barn still stands!

Chapter 26

In the spring of 1990, three of Round Top's prominent citizens, Emmalee Turney, James Dick, and Dr. Jim Ayers, went to see Bill and Frances with a proposition. Since each sponsored events that brought large crowds to Round Top and there were not nearby accommodations, they proposed that the couple open their home as a bed and breakfast. Their answer was an immediate no. But a few glasses of iced tea later, they agreed to a 90 day trial period. From June 1 to September 1 of 1990, Heart of My Heart would be a bed and breakfast.

Bill and Frances saw no harm in trying the arrangement for overnight guests. So many people came to Round Top to enjoy the concerts at Festival Hill, the Shakespeare-at-Winedale Season and the antique fairs in the little town. They found they liked it more than they ever thought. They were surprised at how much they enjoyed the guests. It was like having a party every weekend. And the guests loved it. They came back time after time whether or not there was a concert or other special event, and their 90-day trial period became permanent.

Over time they converted two garages into three more

bedrooms with private baths and remodeled the log cabin to make it more habitable. More and more people came for the weekends. They became new friends, returning frequently, bringing their children and others. The media soon found out about this little ranch nestled in the woods and Heart of My Heart Ranch received a lot of publicity in newspapers, magazines and travel guides.

In 1994, Bill and Frances took a giant step that changed their lives. They turned their hobby/business into their second career. They had more requests from guests than they could accommodate, but didn't know what to do about it. They hated to turn anyone away.

Their next door neighbor, L. E. Simmons, had a 54-acre farm with two fully restored historic houses, a pool and a large workshop. He informed Bill and Frances that he had bought a larger place and asked if they'd be interested in buying his property. Bill and Frances recognized this as a golden opportunity and bought it to expand their bed and breakfast. The houses had been beautifully restored 15 years earlier but were now in need of new everything including-- roofs, air conditioning, bathrooms, furnishings, and septic systems. Bill and Frances set about to remedy the situation, even though it became a financial drain.

Heart of My Heart Ranch now has six houses with 17 bedrooms and baths, a conference center, pool, lake, gardens, horses, donkeys, dogs, cats, lake, boats, golf driving range, playground, hiking trails, five full time employees, and a stiff mortgage. Sometimes they wonder why they work so hard seven days a week, since they don't make any profit, but the answer is because they love the life they have.

Over the years many interesting and funny things have happened to Bill and Frances as they shared their home with guests. In the early years, they would often rent their own bedroom for the weekend and slept on a sleeper sofa in the library. They had put locks on the closet doors so they didn't have to move all their things out.

One spring day, their once a week gardener failed to show up. Frances had bought a pick up truck load of bedding plants and was very upset that the gardener didn't come to help her plant them. All day she worked getting the plants in the ground. Late in the afternoon he finally called.

"Frank, where were you today?" she asked.

Frank, a small man with a very large wife said, "Well, I had trouble at home."

At that, his wife Shirley, took the phone from him. "I'll tell you what all the trouble was. It all started when he took me to work this morning and I found a pair of women's underpants in his truck. I gave him a good beating. Gave him a black eye I did."

Frances didn't know quite what to make of it all, but said her good-byes and hung up the phone. Of course she told Bill about it, but there was nothing they could do.

That night, long after everyone had turned out the lights, Frances continued to toss and turn. The sleep sofa wasn't that comfortable and Frances was very stiff and sore from all the gardening that day. She decided to get in the big outside hot tub even though her swimsuit was locked in the closet, in the bedroom where guests were sleeping. But she really wanted to get into that hot tub to salve her sore muscles.

She laid her nightgown across the porch rail and slipped

nude into the hot soothing water. At that, the young lab, Sara ran up, grabbed her nightgown and ran off with it flapping behind her. Frances got out of the tub and ran back to bed, waking Bill.

"Is everything all right?" he asked.

Still out of breath she said, "Honey, tomorrow if you find my nightgown out in the yard, please don't beat me up."

Another funny story involved a family Bill and Frances are especially fond of. Phil and Lynn Watters and their two little boys called Heart of My Heart their ranch and came many times over a five or six year period. Phil, an avid fisherman would organize all the interested children for a fishing trip to Cummins Creek. They would bring back a bucket of wild bass they caught there and put them in our pond to improve the gene pool. Fishing is a main event here.

One night, Bill and Frances had gone to bed early. Phil decided to try some night fishing. Shortly afterward they were awakened by a loud shout.

"Bill! Bill! Get up! Get up!"

They jumped up thinking something terrible had happened

"Look!" He proudly showed off a 10-pound bass. Bill told him to take it home but he let it go and promised to come back and catch it again.

Another time, Frances was sitting on the pier with Betsy, the mother of four little children The children were fishing while Frances and their mother looked on.

Frances said, "Last year a little child caught a tiny little fish and his foolish mother took it into LaGrange to a taxidermist and spent $65 having it mounted."

Totally unruffled, Betsy said, "Frances, that was me. It was his first fish"

Frances apologized profusely and she and Betsy remained friends.

Once, two little boys were fishing off the pier. They had rigged their line with minnows and red bobbers when one caught a huge bass that weighed in at five pounds and measured 23 inches long. They were so little they had a hard time landing it but finally did by getting the large net and pulling it up on the pier. While they were working on that the second child had put down his pole to help. His minnow was dangling about a foot above the surface of the water when another big bass jumped up out of the pond, took the minnow and the rod and reel and swam off with it. Of course the little boy was very upset.

Matt, then a college boy, working at the ranch for the summer, saw the bobber circling the pond. He got in the johnboat with the net to try to get it. He succeeded in netting the fish then started pulling on the line trying to retrieve the rod and reel, which he did. To everyone's surprise and delight, it had gotten tangled up with another rod and reel that may have been in the lake for years. So on one minnow the boy caught a bass and two poles.

In about 1997, a Mr. Poppe from Fort Worth came by to spend the night. He was an oilman who was working on a nearby well. At 89-years-old, he was very distinguished looking and well spoken. He was alone so we rented him a single room for the night.

He was a great talker and entertained Bill in the living room until 10 that night when Bill excused himself and went to bed. His stories were centered around the early days of the oil business and how he was one of nine Fort Worth oilmen who had founded the Fort Worth Petroleum Club.

In the morning, Bill got up and made some coffee about 5:30 am and found Mr. Poppe fully dressed and ready for the day working on some papers. Bill checked his room to be sure he had not left anything and discovered that Mr. Poppe, a very small man had only slept on 15 inches of the bed.

Bill sat down to figure up what Mr. Poppe owed for the night. "Well, sir, first since you were by yourself, I'll only charge you the single rate. Next, I'm going to give you the senior rate discount and because of your age, I'm going to double that and call it the Super Senior rate. Since you only slept on the far edge of the bed and only used one pillow, you get another discount. Since you entertained me for two hours last night, I'll give you another credit for that. Near as I can tell, after all these discounts and credits, *I owe you $20.00.*"

Mr. Poppe broke into a huge grin and chuckled as he put my $20 into his wallet

As Bill and Frances continue to run their bed and breakfast, they are reminded constantly how small a world we live in. Almost every weekend some of our guests discover they have mutual friends. They learn that they lived in the same small town or worked for the same person, or that their paths have crossed in some other way. Even Bill and Frances have found connections with their guests.

In fact, their very first guests were a couple from Tulsa, Oklahoma. They looked at a picture of G. C. McGregor's, Bill's great grandfather, home in Waco.

The woman said, "My grandmother also lived in Waco

about 1895."

When they turned the picture over, there were the names of the people who attended a party at the McGregor house, and her grandmother was listed as one of the guests.

One memorable occasion involved a young woman, who made a reservation at the ranch but did not want the confirmation mailed, and she paid the deposit with a certified check. When she walked in alone, she had a panic attack when she saw her next-door neighbors were guests. Obviously, the man waiting in the car wasn't her husband. They left in the middle of the night leaving a note saying she wasn't feeling well.

The ranch has played host to a number of weddings since 1990. Most have been casual, simple affairs. Many have been second marriages that have been a combination family reunion and wedding. But occasionally they hose a big, formal affair.

At one, they rented two large tents and a dance floor. There were loads of flowers, food and drink. A white carriage pulled by two white horses delivered the bride and groom from the church to the reception at the ranch and as the bride descended from the carriage with all the guests looking on, up ran Pandy, Bill's year-old lab with a bloody armadillo in her mouth to present to the bride.

The armadillo wasn't dead and was struggling to escape. The video movie cameras were recording it all while the bride tried to dodge the spray of blood. Needless to say, that was the last wedding the dogs attended. Bill and Frances now make sure they're penned up during formal occasions

Bill and Frances could go on for hours about their guests

because they have come to know and love so many of them like family, and all have enriched their lives in so many ways.

From that little one room cabin, Heart of My Heart Ranch has grown to offer additional acreage and buildings with 17 bedrooms, and 20 bathrooms. They can accommodate up to 50 people at any given time and estimate that over the years they have hosted over 22,000 guests, and they still love it.

Through the years and through the tears, Bill's and Frances's story proves that love can and will conquer all Today they live very happily together on their farm and look forward to sharing some of that happiness with their guests

Bill loves to tell his story to all of his guests, the story of how he met his Frances, fell in love with her, lost her, found her, and finally married her. And when he finishes, someone always says, "Bill, you must write a book about this story," and now he has.

You can book your romantic weekend, family vacation, corporate event, or reunion by calling the ranch at 800/327-1242.

Bill and Frances also invite you to visit their website at http://www.heartofmyheartranch.com

About Bill Harris

Born and educated through the 8th grade in New York City, Bill spent the next four years at a military prep school in Staunton, Virginia. He graduated from the University of Texas where he played on the UT Longhorn Football teams of 1949, 1950, and 1951.

After graduation he held the commission of 1st Lieutenant in the US Army between 1954 and 1956. Afterward, he returned to Houston and worked as a life insurance agent for the next 40 years. When he left the insurance company he didn't retire. Instead, he and his wife moved to Round Top, Texas where they have owned and operated a Bed and Breakfast since 1989.

He now spends much of his time writing and helping his wife Frances run their 17 bedroom Country Inn.

About Joan R. Neubauer

Joan R. Neubauer, published in national and regional publications, has written on a variety of subjects including history, camping, nutrition, business, wedding planning, writing, journaling, and personal biographies. A teacher and public speaker, Joan addresses a wide array of subjects for organizations, writers groups, corporations, and has hosted a weekly, thirty-minute, on-the-air writers club near Houston, Texas. In addition, she teaches classes and workshops on the subject of writing, journaling and autobiographies, and hosts a monthly TV segment with Georgetown authors on "Georgetown Roundup," a Cable Channel 10 production.

Joan is the author of *The Complete Idiot's Guide to Journaling, From Memories to Manuscript: The Five-Step Method of Writing Your Life Story,* and *Dear Diary: The Art and Craft of Writing a Creative.* She is also co-author of *Triumph: The Autobiography of Bonnie Pennington,* and *Down But Not Out,* with Houston undercover cop Tom Docherty.

Joan and her husband Steve are the parents of three children and reside in Georgetown, Texas where Joan continues to write, teach, and helps others publish their work. She invites you to email her at JNwriter@aol.com and to visit her website at http://www.io.com/~neubauer.

220

To order additional copies of *Heart of My Heart*

Name _____

Address_____

_____

$19.95 x _____ copies =   _____

Sales Tax   _____
(Texas residents add 7.25% sales tax)

Please add $2.50 postage and handling per book   _____

Total amount due: _____

Please send check or money order for books to:

Heart of My Heart Ranch
Attn: Mr. Bill Harris
P.O. Box 106
Round Top, Texas 78954-5142

Printed in the United States
1971